GEOLOGY EXPLAINED : DARTMOOR AND THE TAMAR VALLEY

IN THE SAME SERIES

Geology Explained in South and East Devon
by John W. Perkins

*Geology Explained in the Severn Vale
and Cotswolds*
and
*Geology Explained in the Forest of Dean
and Wye Valley*
both by William Dreghorn

IN PREPARATION

*Geology Explained in North Devon, Exmoor
and the Quantocks*
Geology Explained in Dorset
Geology Explained in South Wales
Geology Explained in North Wales
Geology Explained in the Lake District
Geology Explained in Yorkshire

GEOLOGY EXPLAINED: DARTMOOR AND THE TAMAR VALLEY

by
JOHN W. PERKINS, BA, FRGS

Illustrations by
the Author

DAVID & CHARLES : NEWTON ABBOT

ISBN 0 7153 5516 3

Set in 11pt Cornell
and printed in Great Britain
by Bristol Typesetting Company Limited Bristol
for David & Charles (Publishers) Limited
South Devon House Newton Abbot Devon

Contents

Introduction

The observer, from a border eminence commanding a far reaching view of the moor, sees before him a vast sweep of dusky rolling hills, with here and there a tor peeping over some dark ridge or cresting some granite-strewn height. Cattle and sheep and ponies browse upon the sides of the hills and in the valleys, but beyond these scarce a sign of life is visible. Few sounds break the stillness, the chief being the cry of the curlew, or the falling waters of some near-by stream. A sense of loneliness possesses the beholder, and he feels he is looking upon a scene from which 'man is far away', and which the ages have done little to alter—*Wm Crossing*

William Crossing, the best known of Dartmoor's early topographers, wrote these words in the introduction to his *A Hundred Years on Dartmoor* (David & Charles reprint 1967). Although we might revise the lines about the absence of life nowadays (in some of the popular areas at least!) we can still share Crossing's deep sense of, and response to, the spirit of Dartmoor, of a great wilderness in the centre of beautiful Devon.

The connections between the moor and the Tamar valley to the west are more intimate than might be expected. Despite the strong contrast of these two landscapes, the reader will find the two districts share many geological episodes in common and, of course, much of the Tamar's eastern drainage originates on Dartmoor.

The Tamar's unique contribution to Westcountry scenery is undoubtedly its middle valley. From a boat on the river, the traveller seems repeatedly to head straight for the towering rock-crowned valley-sides, only to turn hard against them and start off again to the opposite bank to repeat the process. The views from the land are equally impressive. From the top crags of Morwell Rocks a fairy-tale, miniature Rhineland unfolds as you look down on the treetops and twisting river below.

The way the Tamar keeps turning back on itself is easily appreciated lower down on the water's edge. Stand at Morwellham and look across to Calstock Church, high up on the river cliff opposite. With the river running well away to one's left here, it is useful to realise how much it will soon swing back, to pass south of the Church ridge again and reach Calstock's quays.

Crossing was mainly concerned with Dartmoor, but he was very conscious of the proximity of the moor and the Tamar. He reminded his readers that it was only five or six miles from Plaster Down to Morwell Rocks, and that between Buckland Down on the Tavy and Newquay on the Tamar, there is little more than a mile (*Guide to Dartmoor,* p 1).

Both districts are a priceless heritage for those who live in the South West, and also for many who have never visited them. Small wonder that Dartmoor has been named the 'Great Provider'. Over the centuries Devon has prospered with its tin, wool, copper and tourism, and its china clays serve millions of people daily in often unrecognised ways. The Tamar has been equally fruitful, its earlier closely-bound agricultural economy having been thoroughly described in H. P. R. Finberg's *Tavistock Abbey* and its later mining boom in Frank Booker's *Industrial Archaeology of the Tamar Valley.*

The Geological Survey Memoirs for both districts are now rather dated—Dartmoor's was published in 1912 and the Tavistock-Launceston sheet, which covers the central Tamar, in 1911, for example. New editions will undoubtedly come along in time but at present new work by the Institute of Geological Sciences is concentrated on northern areas of Dartmoor and the northern Tamar. New maps for Okehampton and Boscastle have been published, Holsworthy will appear soon, and revision of the Carboniferous stratigraphy in North Devon has been a focus of many geologists' studies.

Remember that Dartmoor is in many ways an open-air laboratory as well as a place of beauty. It is a delicately balanced landscape, the result of centuries of slow evolution. This century man has begun to visit it in greater numbers than the moor has ever known before and with more powerful means of disrupting it than ever before—military explosions, roads busy with cars, cars driven too far off the highway and crushing the plant life. It should not be forgotten that it is an offence to take a vehicle more than 15yd from the roadside, and that land ownership, particularly in the Tamar valley should always be respected. Description here of any site is no passport to access and does not imply that permission will necessarily be forthcoming.

The experienced geologist will need no bidding to respect ownership and obey the country code, but it is still worth reminding ourselves that we must never collect from walls or archaeological remains and must treat all rock exposures with respect. How often a geological party arrives at a site and, as soon as the phenomenon to be seen has been explained, begins to hack up the victim. One piece, obtained by the leader might often be sufficient—most of the other specimens are discarded later anyway. If you genuinely want one to study, look first at the ground below; often there are perfectly good fresh specimens lying there, hacked off for the enjoyment of hammering rather than of geology, and these can usually be readily identified with the outcrop being examined.

It has been assumed throughout that, as the reader sets off to deepen the bonds between himself and these intriguing districts, he will constantly have a compass, a one-inch geological map and a one-inch Ordnance Survey map at hand. As a help, the grid reference and direction of view are given on all illustrations where they may be of use.

> Of making of books there is no end. And as certain as the rivers will ever roll down from the hills of the old moor, so sure is it that men will continue to add to its records. Of what value would these be, could but the rocks tell us their whole story . . . But man has striven, still strives, to make the desert break its silence and to unlock its secrets . . .
> —*A Hundred Years on Dartmoor,* William Crossing.

In a very small way, this book aims to unfold Dartmoor and the Tamar valley.

Chapter 1

The Regional Setting

For at least 4,000 years the upland farming area of Dartmoor has been the home and workplace of men. For centuries it remained isolated and remote, crossed only by a few track-ways, and mainly the concern of those who actually lived within its borders. Man's use of it was limited to what he could make of its surface—stone for houses from the loose clitters on its slopes, peat for fires, tin from simple stream-works, and farming. Admittedly, the climate of the moor was warmer in prehistoric times than now, and farming then included grain cultivation.

The isolation discouraged commerce until a late date, but about 200 years ago the rapid pace of change began to influence Dartmoor. Improved roads and tramways, and a growing population in the rest of Devon, increased the active use of the moor. Now there was granite quarrying rather than the use of surface stone, claypits were opened up on the south-west margins, shaft mining for tin and copper boomed briefly—coupled with improved access to the products and equipment needed.

In this century the growing Westcountry tourist trade, increased military activity, water supply and forestry have sometimes brought conflict in the more intensive demands on the moor. A heritage millions of years old still provides livelihoods, its scenery must be safeguarded, yet a host of other modern requirements must also be met and dealt with. The solutions are no longer the exclusive concern of those who live on the moor. Many living far beyond its borders use its products daily—household water, china clay in medicines, chemical products, glossy-papered magazines and tableware. Dartmoor means far more than a weekend walk or ride and, as the National Park committee strives to remind us, its care is everyone's responsibility, conservationists, archaeologists,

MAP 1

THE REGIONAL SETTING

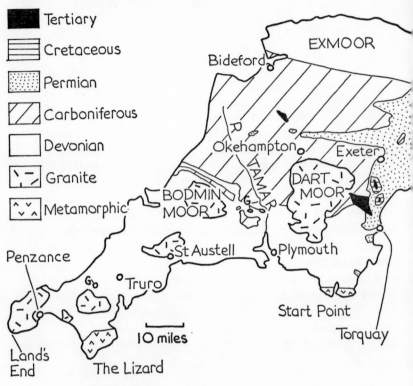

(Generalised from maps of the Institute of Geological Sciences
with permission of the Director)

geologists and naturalists alike, whether or not they have the
special interests of working there.

THE TAMAR VALLEY

The Tamar valley lies west of Dartmoor, draining its
western flanks through two major tributaries, the Tavy and
Walkham rivers and a number of smaller streams. Passing
south over Carboniferous and Devonian beds, highly metamorphosed in places, the Tamar forms a quite distinctive
break in the moorland spine of south-west England, separating Dartmoor from its nearest neighbour Bodmin Moor.
However, considerable lengths of this river system lie well

away from the granites or their associated mineralised districts and the river offers the geologist three quite different studies. The upper valley poses the puzzle described in Chapter 12—rising so near the northern coast, why did the Tamar choose a course to the south almost involving the complete width of the south-west peninsula?

The chief interest of the central districts is the re-appearance of the granites at Kit Hill and Hingston Down near Gunnislake. Abandoned mine workings cover the whole area and make it a mecca for mineral collectors.

The third opportunity for study is offered by the lower reaches of the river, one of the finest rias or drowned estuaries in the South West. Submerged by the most recent change of sea-level, the Flandrian transgression of about 10,000 years ago, much of the lost territory can be seen by the geologist to have already been won back by the Tamar and its tributaries. Over seventy feet of silt already fills the drowned channel beneath the Tamar Bridge and every creek shows how the marshes are creeping further out in their task of reclaiming the submerged landscape.

Perhaps less well-known to tourists than Dartmoor or the more popular estuaries for river trippers such as the Dart, the Tamar valley remains quietly beautiful, many parts of it still only served by narrow lanes. But how well these repay exploring! They lead to views of superb river cliffs and incised meanders, the latter only rivalled in the South West by the Torridge valley in North Devon. There are the jutting crags of Morwell Rocks and of Chimney Rock at Gunnislake or, in complete contrast, the broad lazy bends of the estuary, surrounded by gentle rolling hillsides.

THE GRANITE OUTCROPS OF SOUTH-WEST ENGLAND

A basic feature of both Dartmoor and the Tamar valley is the distribution of the granite outcrops of Devon and Cornwall. All the major moorlands of the peninsula except Exmoor are situated on outcrops of this once molten rock. It was intruded into the Devonian and Carboniferous beds when they were first folded about 290 million years ago, remaining hidden until erosion of those rocks partially revealed its outcrop.

For many years geologists considered each visible area of the granite to be quite separate from the others. The Tamar valley has its own minor outcrops in Kit Hill and Hingston Down, so it was obvious that between Dartmoor and Bodmin Moor at any rate there might be granite not far below the surface. Nowadays geologists are certain that this is so and that all the way down the peninsula the granites are linked. The moorlands are the visible humps or cupolas of a continuous mass, Dartmoor at the eastern end being the highest and largest exposure. The outcrops become lower generally to the west, eventually barely appearing above sea level in the Isles of Scilly. Known as a batholith, the granite mass is believed to end eventually about 100 miles to seaward.

GRAVITY SURVEYS

Information about the extent and continuity of the granite mass is derived from gravity surveys. Gravity, the natural attraction of a large mass for a smaller, is a well-known force, and can be detected by delicate measurements of a pendulum suspended on a string. But if such an experiment was conducted near a mountain mass, the pendulum would not only be pulled downwards by the attraction of earth's gravity, it would also be deflected sideways by attraction to the mountain mass. The greater the rock density of the mountain the more the attraction—a mountain of basalt composition would cause a greater deflection than one of granite, for example.

Similarly with the earth's gravity. Where the crust is largely or solely formed of light-density rock it produces a measurement which is lower than normal, called a negative anomaly. The granite outcrops of the South West are so different in density from the rocks which surround them that they produce a negative anomaly in gravity measurements.

Since measurements in districts between the visible moorland outcrops are also less than would be expected, a continuous body of light-density granite material must be present not far below the surface. The granite continues west of Dartmoor, passing at depth beneath the metamorphosed slates of the eastern Tamar valley. It comes to the surface again just west of the river, then remains hidden until Bodmin Moor is reached.

The Birth oj Dartmoor

The story of the creation of Dartmoor and the Tamar valley begins in the Devonian period, millions of years before the granites were formed or south-west England became land for the first time.

THE GEOGRAPHY OF DEVONIAN TIMES

At the beginning of Devonian times, 400 million years ago, Devon was part of a river flood plain in which the sediments of the earliest known Devonian rocks, the Dartmouth Slates, were formed. This ancient landscape is fully described in Chapter 2 of the author's *Geology Explained in South and East Devon*, David & Charles, 1971. Conditions changed when the coast gradually receded northwards until it lay over South Wales. South-west England was engulfed in a warm ocean which stretched from south-west Eire away to the Ardennes in Belgium, while the rest of Britain to the north was then an arid land.

Coral reefs grew in the ocean and volcanic eruptions occurred periodically. The normal muds and sands of the sea floor accumulated around the reefs and erupted material, and similar conditions continued into the ensuing Carboniferous period—although the amount of reef-building then was less and the thickness of sands formed much greater.

Towards the end of Carboniferous times all the Devonian and Carboniferous material was folded in a major mountain-building period known as the Armorican, or Hercynian. The coral reefs formed limestones, the muds became shale, and with the volcanic ashes and lavas and the great thicknesses of sandstones, the bulk of Devon and Cornwall was born. Today Devonian and Carboriferous sediments account for the area west of a line between Torquay and Bampton in North Devon.

The Tamar valley runs southwards through Carboniferous outcrops to Horsebridge, and then completes its journey to the sea over Devonian beds. In its central districts around Gunnislake the rocks were intruded by the arrival of the granite, or fused and baked by their near-contact with this molten material.

THE AGE AND ORIGIN OF DARTMOOR

The Dartmoor granite arrived as part of the deep-seated intrusion below the folded sediments. The rocks had been fissured and faulted in the folding process and the granite was able to move up along these lines of weakness. It's arrival pushed some of the surrounding folds into new positions, stretching and deforming the rock cover above it. Other rocks were fused and baked by the great heat and some fell into the granite and were absorbed into its own composition.

Geologists date the arrival of the granite at about 290

FIG 1

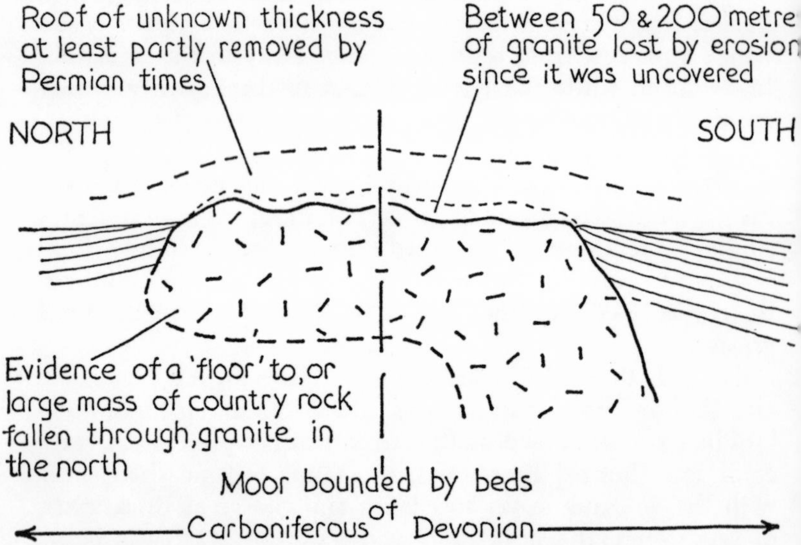

Roof of unknown thickness at least partly removed by Permian times

Between 50 & 200 metre of granite lost by erosion since it was uncovered

NORTH

SOUTH

Evidence of a 'floor' to, or large mass of country rock fallen through, granite in the north

Moor bounded by beds of Carboniferous Devonian

DARTMOOR'S GENERAL STRUCTURE

million years ago. Since the granite was not completely solid when intruded, it was able to move up into a high position in the earth's crust, stoping away some of the rock cover above.

On Dartmoor there is evidence that the granite was also thrusting northwards slightly, shouldering aside folds in the rocks around it. Figure 1 shows that in depth Dartmoor is a normal pluton, steep-sided and cutting across the beds which surround it.

The gravity measurements described in Chapter 1 reveal a peculiar anomaly over northern Dartmoor—interpreted at first as a floor of normal rock about six miles below the granite. Now geologists believe it is caused by a large mass of country rock which broke away and sank down through the granite. In fact, felspar crystals which grew at a late stage sometimes show a parallel alignment, evidence of flow and movement in the granite. Blackingstone Quarry, near Moretonhampstead, is an example but these are only very localised features.

THE COMPOSITION AND VARIETIES OF GRANITE

The great upsurge of geological enthusiasm which occurred at the end of the last century led to a lot of careless, if unintentional damage by specimen collectors and on Dartmoor, as elsewhere, specimens should never be taken from archaeological remains or walls, and only sparingly from rock outcrops. It is usually a good rule to look at something and leave it there for someone else to see, rather than carry it away.

Dartmoor granites have three basic colours : black, grey and either creamy white or pink. Quartz is the glassy grey mineral and when broken up it forms the main part of sands and sandstones. The black glittering material is biotite, or black mica; white mica (muscovite) can also be found in some areas of the moor. Mica and quartz are not of much use commercially, they form the waste dumps of the china-clay industry, but one modern use is as natural aggregates in concrete blocks and in calcium silicate bricks (see Lee Moor, Chapter 7). Known as reformite, the rough faces of the concrete blocks look very similar to natural stone. Sales of the sand tips around Westcountry claypits are also likely to increase as the sources of sand and gravel in southern England become more scarce.

B

The third mineral, felspar, is the most valuable for when decomposed it becomes china clay (see kaolin, below). It is the pink and white varieties of felspar which determine whether granite is red or grey in colour. These three minerals are normally present all over the moor, though in some varieties one of them may have been altered or replaced.

There are two main reasons for the variety of granites seen today. Firstly, areas near the edge of the mass were contaminated by the amount of fragments they absorbed while those well inside it remained more pure. Secondly, there are the mineral changes and replacements which occurred in the

MAP 2

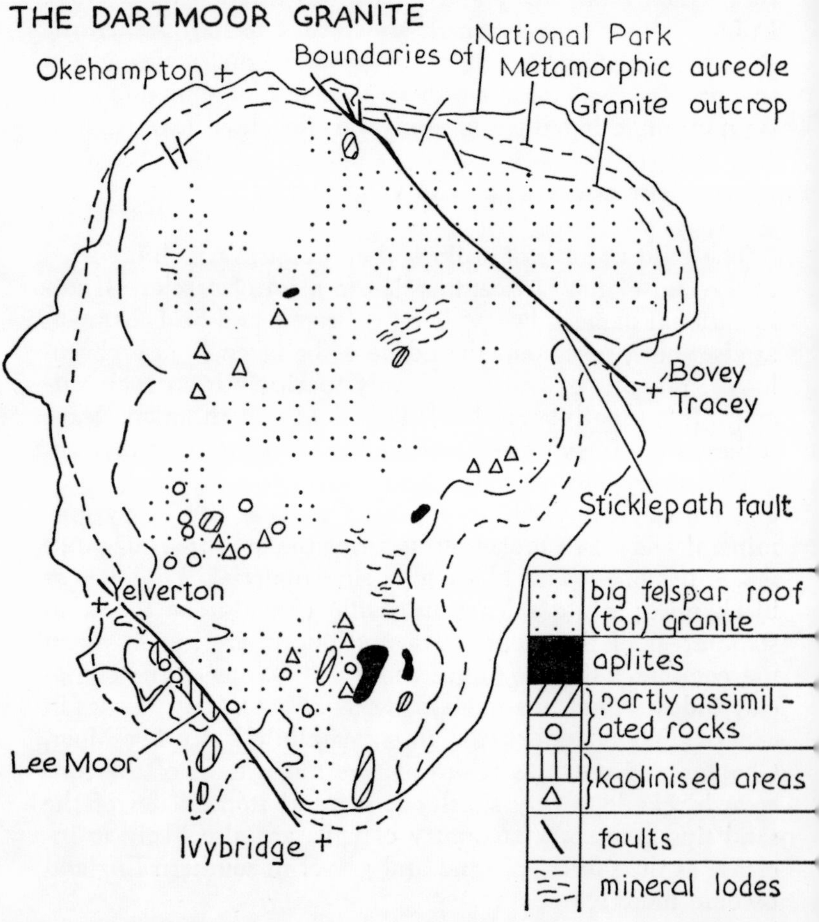

THE DARTMOOR GRANITE

Okehampton

Boundaries of National Park
Metamorphic aureole
Granite outcrop

Bovey Tracey

Sticklepath fault

Yelverton

Lee Moor

Ivybridge

::: ::	big felspar roof (tor) granite
■	aplites
/// o	partly assimilated rocks
⊞ △	kaolinised areas
\	faults
⹈	mineral lodes

gradual cooling down, so a collection of specimens from different areas of Dartmoor soon reveals a surprising range of granites.

The Dartmoor student can begin by making a simple three-fold division :

Tor, or **Giant Granite,** is a coarse-grained rock which was nearest to the roof area. It absorbed large amounts of neighbouring rock and sometimes their altered forms can be recognised in it. It still forms the bulk of the Dartmoor hilltops. Geologists call it a porphyritic granite because it has large crystals of quartz and felspar set in a fine-grained background. The general grain size is over 3mm and the large, opaque white felspar crystals reach 3–5cm in length. These large crystals are known as megacrysts. The upper masses of Hay Tor, Kes Tor and Saddle Tor are good localities for this type.

Quarry, or **Blue Granite,** generally lies beneath the Tor type. Since it was farther from the roof it is less contaminated and its grain size is also smaller, although it is still classed as a porphyritic rock. The grain size in this type is 2–3mm; the felspar megacrysts are fewer in number and only reach 2cm in length. There is more white mica than black. Geologists regard the Quarry granite of the main mass and its rooftop Tor variety as contaminated granites compared to the pure and fine-grained aplites which formed later.

Aplites are fine-grained sheet-like masses. Some of them represent late stages of the intrusion; at Birch Tor, for example, they show chilled edges, indicating that the other granites around them were already much cooler when the aplites arrived. In other cases they are former sandstone bodies absorbed into the granite, and then they have no chilled margins. Aplites are minor features though in comparison to the whole granite area.

The Tor and Quarry granites really gave birth to Dartmoor. Opinions about them vary, some geologists believing they were virtually solid when they arrived, the remaining molten material acting as a lubricant. Others envisage a crystalline mush or a liquid state. Either way, during the later stages there was considerable activity from fluids, gases and steam. Nearness to the roof coupled with these events created the differences between the Tor and Quarry types.

CHANGES DURING COOLING

The masses of watery fluid, rich in silicon and potassium, helped to create the large, white felspar crystals. Combined with the gradual cooling, the fluids and gases also produced other changes. In some localities no sooner had the granite formed than it was under chemical attack from within itself. When the temperature had dropped to 350–400°C, **Greisening** or 'greying' of the granite occurred in places. Hot, acid water circulating in the rock caused the chemical replacement of felspar minerals by white mica (muscovite). Silvery, flaky muscovite finds a use in the home—the heating elements of electric irons, so it is not necessary to search Dartmoor for a sample! It can also be found on Kit Hill, Chapter 15.

Tourmalinisation followed as the temperature continued to fall. Aided apparently by boron gases, tourmaline replaced the black mica, or biotite. Since it appears in black patches or radiating black needles, it seems at first to be much the same as black mica. Fortunately, there is a quick method of distinguishing the two as tourmaline has very fine grooving on its faces. They resemble gramophone records, the grooves running parallel to the long axis of the needles. Tourmaline is commonly found near the margins of the moor.

Kaolinisation also occurred as cooling continued, softening the felspars in some areas to form china clay (kaolin). The steam released began a process of change which gradually extended upwards through the granite, leaving large bodies of soft clay from which the unaltered mica and quartz sand is extracted.

Hot springs and geysers are frequent companions of decaying igneous and volcanic activity today. In those far-off times they could have been generated by the same steam needed to soften the felspars.

The principal claypits on Dartmoor now are those at Lee Moor, though remains of workings exist at several other sites (see Chapter 7).

All the changes and modifications continued eventually with the formation of the mineral deposits.

CHAPTER 3

Dartmoor's Mineral Wealth

The phrase 'Dartmoor's mineral wealth' today means clay minerals (Chapter 7), but in the past it meant metals—tin from the middle ages onwards, and copper in the nineteenth century. Tin was worked both by alluvial streaming and shaft methods and although streaming may seem the more old-fashioned technique, Dartmoor miners brought it to an efficiency which ensured its survival well into the eighteenth century. Copper, on the other hand, was entirely shaft-mined from lodes.

The mineral deposits of the moor were formed from solutions accompanying the fluids and gases described in Chapter 2. The mineral material emerged from the granite at certain points, known as emanative centres, and each of the principal mining districts lies near one of these sources. Geologists used to believe these centres were active just after the formation of the granite itself, but lately they have had to extend the period of mineral formation considerably. Measurements of the age of local radioactive uranium lodes have produced ages as young as 125 to 75 million years, upper Jurassic to Eocene. With the tin lodes formed in Permo-Triassic times, 190 million years ago probably, this means that the history of mineral deposition was in fact a lengthy affair, spread over some 115 million years. An alternative explanation would be a string of successive but quite separate actions.

While the minerals were forming it was, perhaps, a time of hot-spring activity, of geysers, fumaroles and acid waters on the land surface above.

MINERAL ZONES

One key factor in the mineral deposition was the temperature of the surrounding rock. The warm granite played its part

21

at first, but for the later arrivals the nearness of the surface above was probably more important. The result in any case was that the minerals took up a zoned arrangement. Figure 2 shows how tin solidified nearest to the warm granite, then copper, lead and zinc and finally iron in ascending order.

FIG 2

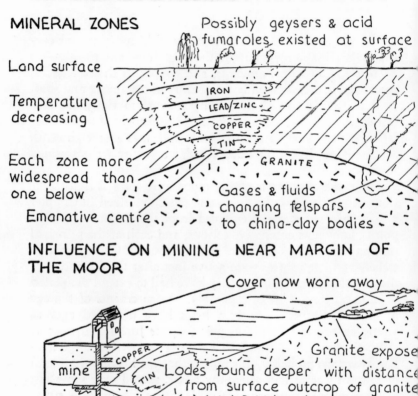

MINERAL ZONES — Possibly geysers & acid fumaroles existed at surface

Land surface

Temperature decreasing

IRON
LEAD/ZINC
COPPER
TIN
GRANITE

Each zone more widespread than one below

Emanative centre

Gases & fluids changing felspars to china-clay bodies

INFLUENCE ON MINING NEAR MARGIN OF THE MOOR

Cover now worn away

COPPER

mine

TIN

Granite exposed

Lodes found deeper with distance from surface outcrop of granite

Even if tin has formed here mine may be too far 'off-centre' to find it

It is an idealised picture though for the full sequence is never found, sometimes because the centre did not produce all the necessary components in its emanations, sometimes perhaps because later erosion has removed the upper deposits already. There are anomalies, too, which at first seem to discredit the whole concept of zoning; for example, hematite (an iron ore) is plentiful in the dumps of Vitifer and Golden Dagger tin mines south of Warren House Inn. But this is the variety known as specular hematite. It is full of grey, glittering mica-like facets which forced it to solidify in the lower tin zone instead. (See Birch Tor, Chapter 8).

A famous Cornish mine, Dolcoath, commenced in copper and changed to tin with depth, but this was rare. It had its influence on other Westcountry mines though (Devon Great Consols for example, p 154), landowners hoping that their copper mines would also change deep down. Apart from the probable absence of tin originally, failure could also stem from the wider spread of each mineral zone compared to the one below it. As Figure 2 shows, a copper mine could be too far from the emanative centre to have tin beneath.

The same figure also illustrates how the temperatures at the time caused the ores to solidify with upper limits almost

FIG 3

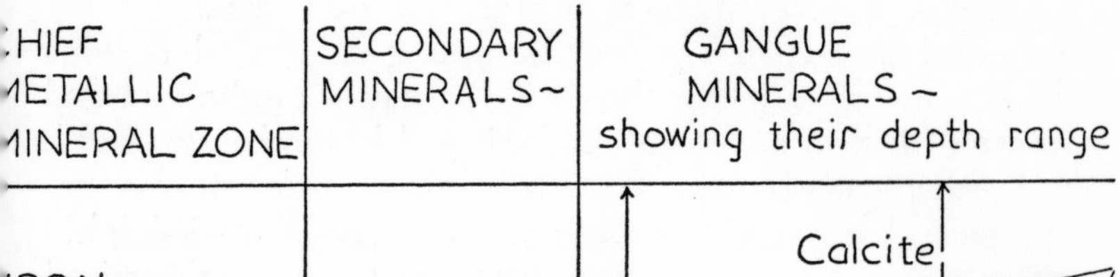

CHIEF METALLIC MINERAL ZONE	SECONDARY MINERALS ~	GANGUE MINERALS ~ showing their depth range
IRON nearest surface		Calcite
LEAD/ZINC	May bear SILVER	Quartz Barytes Fluorspar
COPPER	ARSENIC LIGHT GREY	Chlorite—pale-green soft &
TIN deepest zone	WOLFRAM BLACKISH	Tourmaline

GROUPING OF MINERALS IN THE MAIN ZONES

parallel to the granite surface. As a result, miners working around the margins of the moors often had to follow the lodes downwards as they worked outwards from the granite.

Two more groups of minerals accompanied the metallic deposits—the gangue and accessory groups. The gangue minerals acted as a flux, helping the metals to migrate upwards. Quartz is the most common gangue mineral and veins of it are found all over Devon in all types of rock. The accessory minerals are those of secondary importance : the arsenic found in copper zones and the wolfram (tungsten) from the tin zone, so important in the manufacture of hard steel. The general arrangement of the major groups is shown in Figure 3.

NEW CONCEPTS ON MINERAL DEPOSITION

Before leaving the subject of mineral zones and their origin, it is well to note that these ideas are now becoming rather old-fashioned and incorrect. As mentioned above, geologists have already had to extend the time scale for mineralisation considerably. In consequence, the granite must have already solidified and cooled before the youngest mineral deposits had even formed! Was there an alternative mechanism and control in these late stages? If so, it still has to be discovered.

Further information, which also seems to contradict the old ideas, has come from study of the Tregonning-Godolphin granite in Cornwall. If it were true that the minerals arrived soon after the granite, then they ought to be present during the final stages of granite formation. They should be moving up through it, ready for release. But these studies show that right at the close of the Tregonning-Godolphin granite's formation there is no evidence of an enrichment by tin, copper or zinc.

So, much clearly remains to be discovered about our South West mineral lodes, and it is possible to speculate—but only speculate—on some dramatic possibilities. For example, could the periods of mineralisation be associated with the stress and friction in the earth's crust caused by the widening of the Atlantic when Europe and North America prepared to drift apart? The theory of continental drift is an old one but it has now been proved, and geophysicists put the Atlantic event at about 80-120 million years ago.

DARTMOOR MINING DISTRICTS

Several emanative centres are known on and around the Dartmoor granite. The more important ones are easily recognised by the amount of mining activity they created in the past—Mary Tavy and Birch Tor, for example, but Dartmoor

MAP 3

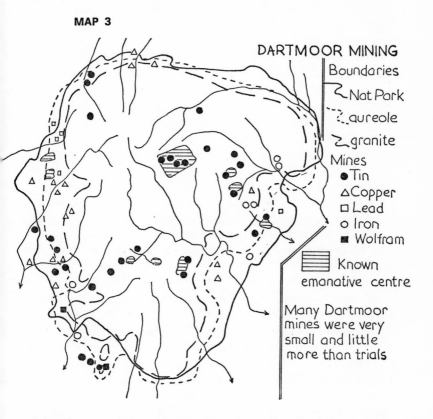

DARTMOOR MINING

Boundaries
⌇ Nat Park
⌇ aureole
⌇ granite
Mines
• Tin
△ Copper
▢ Lead
○ Iron
▣ Wolfram

▤ Known
emanative centre

Many Dartmoor mines were very small and little more than trials

generally was never as important as the Cornish mining districts to the west. Map 3 shows the known centres and the distribution of the Dartmoor mines by their chief mineral product.

The majority of Dartmoor lodes lie E.NE–W.SW and are tin- or copper-bearing. They occur in the granite outcrop and in the metamorphosed Devonian and Carboniferous beds which surround it. One feature which distinguishes the Dartmoor tin lodes from those in Cornwall is the occurrence in them of

specular hematite and its softer usable form, micaceous hematite. The latter was worked until recently at Hennock (page
101) and a lot of specular hematite can be found in the dumps
south of Warren House Inn. (Chapter 8.)

Although less common than tin, the Dartmoor copper lodes
have been very productive, notable mines being Devon Friendship at Mary Tavy, Wheal Franco at Horrabridge and Wheal
Emma near Buckfastleigh. The copper bodies lie away from
the granite outcrop.

The principal lead lodes found have again been at Mary
Tavy (Wheal Betsy) and along the Teign valley southwards
from Bridford. Wheal Betsy's ore was silver-bearing like that
of Bere Alston, and of Combe Martin in North Devon.

A rough summary can be made of the mineral lodes on
various parts of Dartmoor :

Northern Dartmoor: only a few small tin mines occur in
the granite. Mineralisation here is in the metamorphosed
Carboniferous rocks and in the form of enriched beds rather
than true lodes, eg, the copper mines at Belstone and Ramsley.

Southern Dartmoor: variable tin lodes in quartz-tourmaline
veins, typical of the deeper parts of the tin zone. Shaft mining
has never been economic at depth on this part of the moor
and over the centuries alluvial or stream tin output must have
been the greater here.

Western Dartmoor: mainly east-west copper lodes, occurring in the metamorphic aureole, with notable north-south
cross-courses containing lead at Wheal Betsy and Crelake. Tin
production from shaft mines in the granite and the aureole
has been small, but there was considerable early streaming in
the Plym and Meavy valleys. The south-west area around
Hemerdon has provided a little of every metal from its small
lodes, including wolfram. The modern china-clay workings
occur in this area at Lee Moor, (Chapter 7).

Central Dartmoor: mineralisation here is again typical of
the deeper parts of the tin zone as in southern Dartmoor, but
with a great deal of specular hematite. Again like southern
Dartmoor, an area of variable values with a good deal of
opencast working and only relatively shallow shafts.

Eastern Dartmoor: includes the last mine worked in Devon,
the Great Rock micaceous hematite mine at Hennock. Around
Ashburton, copper and umber were important (working of the

latter is fully described in *Geology Explained in South and East Devon*). A north-south lead and barytes lode was worked in the Teign valley, and at Haytor magnetite iron ore. Chagford was another important tin-streaming area and shaft mining there proved that the tin on that part of Dartmoor was present in stockworks, masses of quartz-tourmaline veins rather than true lodes.

Important mines in each of these districts are described in the regional surveys of Dartmoor, Chapters 6 to 9, and 11.

There are few visible relics of shaft-mining on the Dartmoor skyline today, most of the old engine-houses have been demolished and the shafts fallen or filled in. It takes a practised eye to sort out the layout of a mass of overgrown leats, buddles, calciners, and stamping-floors which are the more common but less obvious relics. On the moorland ridges there are dozens of old trench-like excavations. These were probably used to work the poor, shallow tin lodes, lodes too unreliable to risk shaft development. In contrast to these trenches, the valleys contain extensive hummocky ground, scenery which can be traced back to the older tin-streaming activities. The tin miners' contributions to the shape of many Dartmoor valleys, late man-made changes in a long geological history, must not be overlooked. However, as explained later, it is doubtful whether they can also be accused of destroying the moor's peat cover.

MINING AND JOINTS

No visitor to Dartmoor can fail to be impressed by the massive joints which cleave the granite tors. Of course the joints exist near the surface over the whole moor, and it is only erosion which has made them such a noticeable feature of the exposed surfaces. Apart from their influence on the tors (Chapter 5) they also played an important role in mineralisation. On Dartmoor the joints follow two main vertical directions, w.sw to e.ne and n.nw to s.se, known as the east-west and north-south joints for simplicity. The east-west group seem to have formed first and those nearest escaping mineral solutions were filled with lodes of tin and copper. Later, the lead-zinc ores moved up into the north-south joints. Mary Tavy (Chapter 6) serves as an illustration with the workings of its Devon Friendship copper mine lying east-west, while those of Wheal Betsy lead mine are north-south.

Experienced moor-walkers are unlikely to take mining reference books with them but they will, of course, carry a compass, so here is a ready means of determining the metal worked at any new site visited. Find the alignment of the old shafts. If they run east-west it was a tin or copper mine, but if north-south the product was lead, zinc, and possibly silver.

TIN STREAMING

The great tin-streaming periods were in the fifteenth, sixteenth and eighteenth centuries. In the middle ages demand for the metal had been high, for pewter manufacture, bell-founding and other purposes. Many household goods were made of pewter, an alloy of tin with about 6 per cent antimony and up to 2 per cent of lead.

The miners worked the broad, gravelly basins of the moor where the heavy tin-bearing stones and crystals of cassiterite could be dug or washed out.

Stream tin tends to be pure and more easily smelted than lode tin since it has already been separated from most of its waste during its transport by rivers. Hence the effectiveness in their day of the simple smelting arrangements of the blowing houses, although their product would seem very gravelly by modern standards.

The old miners knew tin by three names, depending on where they found it—stream, shode and mine. 'Mine' and 'stream' need no further explanation. Shodes were the concentration of bigger tin-stones found in the river bank near the parent lode. The 'old men' had a wonderful appreciation of scenery and rock type, and discovered most of what was worth having. They would study the moor intimately, learning to recognise the types of stone and colours of the soil so that they could trace them up river from their streamworks. Thus they would gradually find the shode stones and, eventually, the parent lode from which both shode and stream gravels had come.

Lode mining was very difficult in the earlier periods because they could not solve the problem of drainage. But if they did not succeed far below ground, on the surface at least they were great hydraulic engineers, able to move vast quantities of material by ingenious use of water power. A considerable amount of dead ground had to be processed for the heavy tin stones usually lay at the bottom of at least 20 to 36ft of gravel. The river had to be diverted first and then a trench sunk to the level (Figure 4). A quarry face could then be set up and the trench moved forward, the tinners throwing the waste behind them as they went.

FIG 4

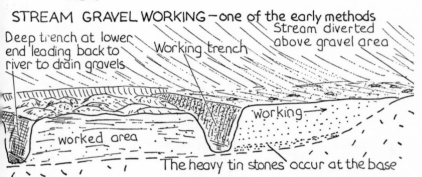

STREAM GRAVEL WORKING — one of the early methods
Stream diverted above gravel area
Deep trench at lower end leading back to river to drain gravels
Working trench
working →
worked area
The heavy tin stones occur at the base

They also used water to discover lodes, running a leat along the hillside and letting it run back to the river at various points. The water scoured channels down the slopes, revealing any lodes in the bed-rock below.

Lode tin has never been very rewarding on Dartmoor, unfortunately. The very erosion which created the stream-tin beds inevitably destroyed a good part of the lode resources.

Water was also essential to the tin dressing, the sequence of sorting, crushing and washing which got rid of the waste before the ore was smelted. To sort the gravels, they made use of the circular motion of water, or raked them against streams of water passing along narrow wooden channels. In the end this produced a concentrate, the lighter waste being washed away. The concentrate was then taken to the blowing house for smelting. Figure 5 shows the general arrangement of the blowing houses which probably replaced the simple clay-covered smelting heap from the fourteenth century onwards. Ruins of these are found on many parts of the moor.

FIG 5

THE DARTMOOR BLOWING HOUSE

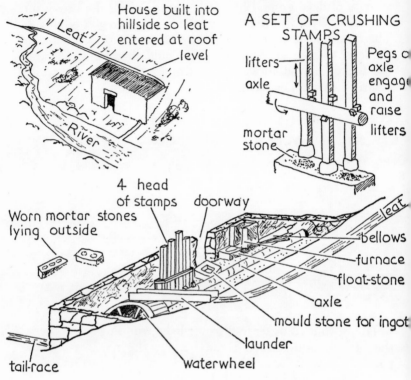

House built into hillside so leat entered at roof level

A SET OF CRUSHING STAMPS

lifters — axle

Pegs o axle engag and raise lifters

mortar stone

4 head of stamps   doorway

Worn mortar stones lying outside

leat

bellows

furnace

float-stone

axle

mould stone for ingot

launder

tail-race   waterwheel

House usually 30–32 ft by 15–17 ft

You can still pan for tin in Dartmoor streams (armed with appropriate permissions!) although working upstream through the gravels is hardly likely to produce any bonanzas in the shodes along the banks.

On the moor today streams eddying around bends or large boulders perform this separation naturally. These disturbed areas are the place to look for black tin crystals. Tin-bearing gravels also occur beyond the moor on old river terraces—there is a workable deposit near Buckfastleigh. The Aller Gravels near Newton Abbot are tin-bearing and could be worth working as a bulk mineral for tin and gravel sales.

MAP 4

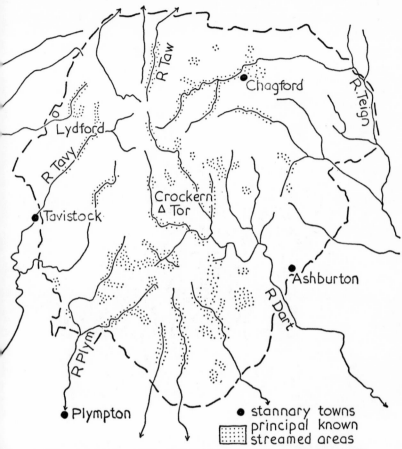

TIN STREAM-GRAVEL WORKING ON DARTMOOR

TIN STREAMING AND SCENERY

Modern proposals for opencast mining on Dartmoor would rightly raise howls of protest in many quarters. The tin streamers influence on the scenery is still very obvious, hardly a moorland valley escaped their attention. The Chagford area and the Plym and Meavy valleys were particularly important centres. Map 4 attempts to show the extent of their influence. At all these sites the typical hummocks of worked gravel are seen; often, as a Cadover Bridge, extending into a marked cut along the base of the hillsides. Looking exactly like the edges of river-terraces, these cuts mark the limits of the old diggings.

Chapter 4

The Surface of the Moor

Dartmoor scenery has a unique fascination. True, there are many other rugged uplands in Britain to attract the eye and Dartmoor may share with them its peaty soils, rough grasses and bracken. But none can rival its tor-crowned ridges or the broad, rolling basins where so many Devon rivers rise. The origin of the tors is considered more fully in Chapter 5.

Many events have shaped the surface of the moor since it formed beneath a cover of Devonian and Carboniferous rocks. At first, the granite remained hidden and a long period of erosion began, forming the New Red Sandstones so prominent in the Exe Valley and along the Torquay-Budleigh Salterton coast. The St Cyres Beds, lying north of the moor, accumulated about the middle of this period and they contain the first xenoliths which could have come from the granite. At least a part of it must have been exposed by then.

The rock roof was slowly worn away until Cretaceous times, when the first event to make a major contribution to the surface of the moor occurred. The sea extended westwards, passing over the moor not far above the present hilltop levels. This was the submergence which produced the great unconformity which is such a feature of East Devon. The submergence was a brief one as far as Dartmoor was concerned. The thin veneer of rock it produced was soon worn away again, but the present river pattern is a legacy of the event.

The sea's retreat left an eastward sloping floor, a surface on which the earliest Dartmoor rivers were soon at work. The easterly direction is visible today, particularly in the upper Dart and Teign. The erosion of these early rivers created an upland surface still seen around High Willhays, Great Links Tor and Cranmere Pool. Including the tors left on it, this surface now stands at 1,500-1,900ft. From this point in time there are two opposing theories about Dartmoor's history.

THE SOUTHERLY TILT AND UPLIFT

This began with a period of earth movements, extending into mid-Tertiary times. The movements explain why Dartmoor now has two distinct sources for its streams, Cranmere Pool is central to the Dart, Teign, West Okement and Tavy of the northern moor while in the lower southern area the Plym, Yealm, Erme and Avon rise around Duck's Pool. During the movements the Alps were formed in Europe but in England the effects were minor. In the South West it meant the re-folding and adjustment of existing folds and the appearance of a series of tear-faults (Chapter 11). On Dartmoor, there was a new and uneven uplift which tilted the upland to the south. Combined with the original eastward drainage, it produced a number of striking effects on the scenery.

One result is this difference in summit heights between the northern and southern moor. The 1,500-1,650ft height in

FIG 6

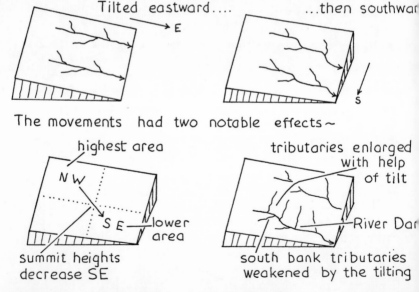

Tilted eastward....   ...then southward

The movements had two notable effects ~

highest area
NW
SE — lower area
summit heights decrease SE

tributaries enlarged with help of tilt
River Dart
south bank tributaries weakened by the tilting

EFFECTS OF EARTH MOVEMENTS ON DARTMOOR

the south is really part of the 1,500-1,900ft surface to the north, but tilted to a lower level. Similarly, it reveals why the highest part of the moor is in the north-west, for this would be the highest district both in the original easterly slope and the later southerly one.

The Ordnance Survey one-inch tourist map of Dartmoor, an indispensable companion to any study of the upland, reveals a third effect. The A384 Princetown-Ashburton road follows the north side of the Dart for much of its journey. From this bank the West Dart receives long tributaries, the Black Brook, East Dart, Walla Brook and others. The south-

MAP 5

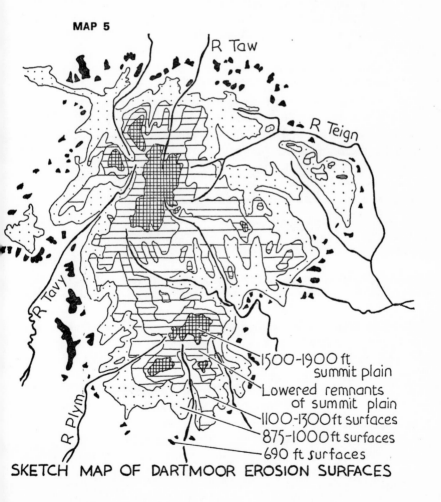

SKETCH MAP OF DARTMOOR EROSION SURFACES

ward tilt heped each of them to enlarge its valley, giving it
renewed gradient and power. But on the opposite bank the
reverse was true. The Swincombe and the O Brook found
themselves fighting an increasingly uphill battle to reach
northwards to the Dart, so their modern valleys are much
smaller.

The tilting also favoured the development of the southern
Dartmoor river system, the Plym, Erme, Avon and Yealm,
while all over the moor rivers began a new phase of erosion
producing several levels between 700 and 1,350ft. The upper
limit of brown colouring on the tourist map gives a good visual
impression of the 1,000ft level (see p 99). Corndon, Laughter
and Bellever Tors are among the hill remnants which survived on these new surfaces.

Geologists believe that all these higher surfaces were the
work of land conditions and that not until the close of Tertiary
times did the sea again play a role. This was in the advent of
the 690ft sea which made Dartmoor an island in early Ice
Age times. Falling away in a 'staircase' of pauses, it produced a series of lower surfaces before it stopped at its present
height. Some of the best fragments of the 690ft surface can be
seen around western Dartmoor (Chapter 6). Once it had re-
treated Dartmoor was broadly in modern form, though the
sea still had much work to do elsewhere in Devon.

ALTERNATIVE IDEAS

From many Dartmoor hillsides the walker can gaze over
the Devon countryside below and, seen from above, the most
notable impression is of a plateau. Broad level ridges and
valleys, obviously cut down from common levels, are so extensive that some geologists believe the high sea levels could
not possibly have formed them in so short a time as the million
years since the Ice Age began. For them, there must have been
a different sequence of events.

Beginning as far back as Permo-Triassic times, the unroof-
ing of Dartmoor would be accompanied by a substantial
shaping of the surface we know today. Secondly, regarding
the effect of the southward tilting, they believe it began much
earlier, helping the Tamar, for example, to establish its course
down to Plymouth. But the climax of the movements (the

formation of the Alps etc) saw their effect on Devon change to a gentle warping—downwards in mid-Devon, upwards in south Devon (Figure 52).

This is a very satisfying theory when the student ponders why the Tamar now flows south to pass through higher ground between Dartmoor and Bodmin Moor rather than going directly to the sea in the Bristol Channel. It is because it was already flowing south at the time of the warping. The river cut its southern valley deeply into the countryside as South Devon and Cornwall rose around it, rather like keeping the knife still and pushing the cake up from underneath.

Another interesting feature is the climate of Tertiary times. During the warping it was tropical, a time of deep, chemical weathering, which could have substantially completed the shaping of the landscape before the 690ft sea came along.

The last difference to note is that there is also a dispute about the highest point reached by these Ice Age seas. Many would prefer a maximum in the South West of 430ft rather than 690ft.

For the present, both histories must be considered, but the second does seem to relate the origin of Dartmoor's surface more satisfactorily to the geological events.

WEATHERING ON DARTMOOR

There are two major methods of wearing away the land surface, mechanical and chemical. Mechanical weathering includes erosion by running water and the freezing and splitting action of frost, but chemical weathering depends on the actual breakdown and alteration of the minerals in a rock. The success of each depends on the composition of the rock concerned.

Dartmoor has suffered the attentions of both in its long history. Ignoring for the moment the effect of its joint systems, the moor's reaction to them can be roughly summarised as follows. Because it is a homogeneous rock, it is not very susceptible to the ordinary action of running water, so the present river erosion on the moor has hardly done much damage. The streams have simply followed ready-made basins.

However, while granite is a uniform material from a mechanical viewpoint, it is far from immune to chemical weathering because of its three different minerals : quartz, felspar and mica. Chemical weathering has done great damage to Dartmoor. It was particularly active during the decomposition following the arrival of the granite (page 20), in the Eocene period when hot savanna conditions existed in Devon and the Aller Gravels near Newton Abbot were formed and, again, in the warm interglacial periods of the Ice Age.

It is when the effect of the natural jointing in the granite is added to the picture that the extent of Dartmoor's weaknesses is discovered. The east-west and north-south vertical joints, forming soon after the arrival of the granite, have already been described in connection with the mineral deposits, but there are also strong horizontal joints.

FIG 7

TOR FEATURES

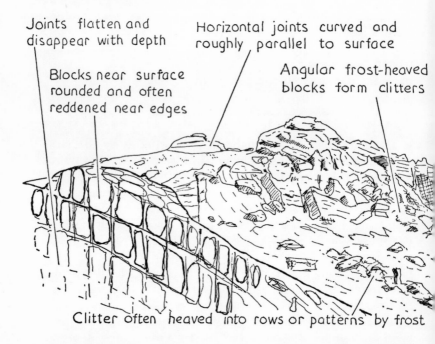

Joints flatten and disappear with depth

Horizontal joints curved and roughly parallel to surface

Blocks near surface rounded and often reddened near edges

Angular frost-heaved blocks form clitters

Clitter often heaved into rows or patterns by frost

Geologists link their formation to the removal of the old rock roof which covered the moor; loss of this great weight allowed an upward adjustment in the light density granite, so the horizontal joints are known as stress-release joints. On tors like Blackingstone they appear curving parallel to the surface but they do flatten out and eventually disappear with depth.

The various joint systems allowed chemical weathering to penetrate more deeply into the granite, reddening and rounding the blocks. Opened up in this way the joints were then more ready than ever to succumb to frost action, particularly, as described below, in the intensely cold phases of the Ice Age.

Both mechanical and chemical weathering continue on the moor today. Rainwater, mixing with carbon dioxide to give weak carbonic acid, can break down the granite minerals, and acids from peaty soils help its work. The squarish granite blocks develop a reddened and rounded outer margin wherever they are found on or near the surface. Digging downwards, they reveal joints which are still fresh and narrow.

The rotted granite produced can be seen in joints and under peat soils all over the moor. Known as 'growan', it is composed almost entirely of quartz, all its clay-forming felspars have been washed away.

DARTMOOR IN THE ICE AGE

One of the great attractions of Devon and Cornwall to geologists is the fact that these counties are the only parts of highland Britain which were never covered by ice-sheets. The nearest sheets reached a line between Bristol and London, so here there are no clay drifts to mask the solid-rock geology below.

But Devon was very cold, sub-Arctic. There must have been a cover of ice on the moor, although it was not enough to start glacier movements. On the north coast of Devon and Cornwall, icebergs breaking away from sheets covering the Irish Sea were floating in and melting on the shores. They left boulders of rocks quite foreign to this area—Scottish granites, for example, were dumped on the Devon coast in this fashion.

During the Ice Age there were rapid and extreme changes of climate, and the results of these climatic see-saws can be seen all over the moor today. Between the four major cold phases it was sometimes as warm as it is nowadays in East

FIG 8

HEN TOR : PLYM VALLEY 587648 NE

Broad rolling ridge
1500 ft summit level
of southern moor

Tor almost reduced
to pile of loose
boulders

Huge field of angular clitter
moving away down slopes

Africa—rhinoceros and hippopotamus once roamed Devon. Like the warm climates of Tertiary times, these warmer phases were periods of chemical rotting of the granite.

Each time the climate turned cold again frost and ice action, finding the granite already weakened, began splitting, heaving and sludging away vast quantities of loosened material. During the brief summers the top soil, thawing out to a depth of a foot or two, became the scene of repeated earth flows. The result of these flows are recorded as 'Head' on the geological maps, and their contribution to the coastal scenery is described in *Geology Explained in South & East Devon*.

Masses of hillside material were washed away down the moorland slopes. The Dartmoor tors, previously just rotting away below the surface, were now left bare and exposed as the loose rubble around them disappeared. Water finding its way into their joints froze and expanded, pushing the blocks downhill in great fields of stones—the Dartmoor clitters. Hen Tor in the Plym Valley is a good site at which to inspect clitter formations and some of these features are described in detail later.

It was the Ice Age, then, which produced the most recent changes in the tors, slopes and clitters. Its mechanical destruction altered a moorland already broadly shaped by earth movements and erosion surfaces, and in detail weakened by selective chemical changes.

THE PEAT COVER OF DARTMOOR

The peat cover of Dartmoor must rank as a major part of the visual impression left with the visitor. Everyone who walks over the remote areas will be familiar with the black deposits, but those who stay near the main roads and lower districts see little more than the black colour. The peat is surprisingly shallow over much of the granite outcrop.

The peat growth is a recent feature. It began to develop in Post-Glacial times, in the Neolithic and Bronze Age periods, about 3,000-500 BC. The moor had warmed up after the Ice Age; climatically, it was at its best about 5,000-3,000 BC and plant life improved from poor heath to deciduous woodland.

Botanists can determine the frequency of various plants by counting the occurrence of each one's pollen grains, preserved in the peat and earth deposits of a given period. This pollen

FIG 9

CUTTING PEAT   Dartmoor peat was cut in thin turves compared to the thicker Irish blocks

Tie up to 40ft in

length

Depth up to 4ft

A turfing iron

Right angled edge used against face of tie

analysis shows that the Dartmoor woodland developed from hazel to oak and elm, perhaps with open heath still present in the highest districts.

It was here that the peat began to grow in blanket bogs. Prehistoric man helped the process with his destruction of the forest, increasingly in the Bronze Age, and growth was also helped by a change to a colder and wetter climate around 500 BC. The peat has prevented the roots of other plants reaching the soil below. Only those fond of a damp home can survive on it—chiefly cotton-grass and sphagnum—and it effectively prevents much improvement of the present grazing.

If any forest survived from prehistoric times in the valley bottoms and along the moorland margins, the tin streamers would have completed its disappearance in their search for fuel.

Today it seems tempting to get rid of the peat, but this would produce other disasters. The peat cover acts as a giant sponge, storing millions of gallons of water which would otherwise run rapidly off the granite and cause serious flood damage elsewhere in Devon.

In dry periods the water seeps slowly from the peat, regulating water supply and giving the moor a very good dry-weather run-off. So the peat cover must be preserved against dangers such as excessive burning or over-grazing.

The effect of the peat cover on the granite below is small. Rainwater passing through it does become weak carbonic acid, but the chemical weathering which results is very little in the present temperate climate. In fact, the peat is probably a protection for the rock beneath it.

The surprising feature of the Dartmoor peat is its shallow depth. The blanket bog exceeds 2ft only over ground above 1,500ft, and valley bogs more than 12ft in depth are very limited. The tinners were not to blame for the destruction of valley peat for, of course, they only worked the gravelly basins —relatively well-drained valleys where little peat would have accumulated anyway.

Whatever the site, once the peat is broken by channels, erosion and decay begin. Peat gullies are potential trouble spots, and walkers crossing them should take care not to break down the sides. Badly eroded bogs can be seen at Cranmere Pool and on the slopes of Great Kneeset.

PEAT AS A FUEL

Peat has been a valuable fuel for tinners and more perma-
nent residents alike. Its fixed carbon content is the measure
of its use and R. H. Worth provides comparative figures in
his *Dartmoor*—wood 17% fixed carbon, grass 19%, peat 29%,
lignite (brown coal, eg, the Bovey Beds in South Devon) 40%,
bituminous coal 65%, anthracite 80-94%. 1.8-2lb of air-dried
peat is equivalent to 1lb of coal.

MAP 6

PEAT CHARCOAL WORKING : N DARTMOOR   after Woolner

The tinners used peat to make charcoal for their blowing
houses, burning the dried bricks in large mounds (meilers)
sealed over with turf and mud. In the sixteenth century Dartmoor charcoal was carried as far as St Austell. Remains of
the industry occur on northern Dartmoor, perhaps account-
ing for a depletion in prehistoric remains there and certainly
interrupting the natural evolution of the moor's surface
deposits long before the present extensive military disturbance.

The main charcoal working sites, shown on Map 6, were
Okement Hill, Wild Tor Ridge, Hangingstone Hill, Quentin's
Man, Hew Down, Taw Head, Fordsland Ledge, Dinger Plain,
Curtery Clitters, White Horse Hill, Winneys Down and Kitty
Tor.

The industry continued until at least 1826 and affected an
estimated 2,000 acres. At a consumption of 12,000 bushels of
charcoal (moor-coal) a year, a 4ft depth of peat would supply
700 blowing house/years.

Dartmoor peat charcoal was also used by moorland black-
smiths, producing a tough iron with no blisters in it.

CHAPTER 5

The Dartmoor Tors

Special reference must be made to the Dartmoor tors since they are the moorland's most unusual feature. However, their importance does not stem from a history which differs from the moorland surface as a whole. They share its record of chemical and mechanical weathering.

The geological interest of the tors lies in the problem of deciding which of these two forms of weathering was principally responsible for tor formation. Some geologists believe in a chemical origin while others see mechanical means as the more important.

THE NATURE OF THE TORS

Dartmoor tors have been graphically described as 'cyclopean masonry', and a first acquaintance with one can destroy quite a few misconceptions about them. Seen from a parking point somewhere on the road below, the slopes may look deceptively smooth and inviting to climb. The ascent begins, and soon you are leaping and scrambling over fields of stones of all shapes and sizes. The summit disappears from view several times as you wend your way through the larger clitter, and smaller blocks suddenly wobble and throw you off in haste to find a more secure footing.

Eventually the base of the tor is reached and those with a head for heights seek a way to the top. The true size of the blocks becomes very apparent now at close quarters and in some cases it is almost impossible to get up onto them. There may be surprises in store when you do—a logan stone perhaps, or, as is frequently the case, a much steeper drop than you had imagined on the far side. Fortunately the tors are so varied that even the least energetic climber can find one that will suit his needs, and it is from the top of a tor that the nature

FIG 10

HOUND TOR 739731 E

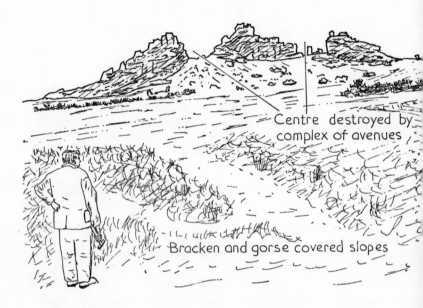

Centre destroyed by complex of avenues

Bracken and gorse covered slopes

of these unusual piles and their relationship to the moorland surface can best be appreciated.

On every side the wide expanses of the moor undulate away in broad ridges and troughs, and distance becomes deceptive. How often the newcomer decides to make for another tor 'just across the valley' and finds a lengthy walk in front of him. Stand, for example on Trowlesworthy Tors above Lee Moor, (Figure 11). The view northwards is very characteristic and Sharpitor, Leather Tor, North Hessary, Cox and Staple Tors are a few of those to be seen. An added attraction here is the red granite which outcrops along the Trowlesworthy ridge (page 116), and a short walk north eastwards over Willings Walls Warren brings the geologist to a fine vantage point for the extensive clitters around Hen Tor, (Figure 8).

The Trowlesworthy granite has a quite distinctive character. Its colour is due to its pink felspars, mixed with plenty of white

mica and quartz. It survived decomposition despite its nearness to the kaolinised area of Lee Moor, perhaps because of
its different mineral composition. Ironically, it is easily
attacked by frost, a fact readily appreciated by anyone visiting
these particular tors. While there, a search can be made for
the fine-grained felsite which the granite passes into in places,
and for white felspar phenocrysts, though these are rare at
Trowlesworthy.

FIG 11

TROWLESWORTHY TORS 580640 NNW

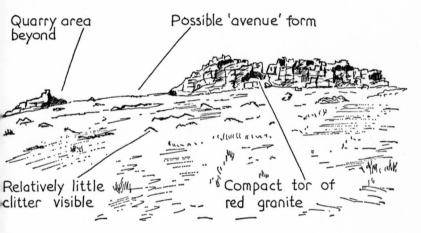

Quarry area beyond

Possible 'avenue' form

Relatively little clitter visible

Compact tor of red granite

WEATHERING AND TORS

Every Dartmoor tor must have experienced both mechanical
and chemical weathering to some degree. Chemical weathering of the granites was intensive in the decomposition following their arrival and in the warm climates of Tertiary times,
while mechanical weathering was dominant in the Ice Age.

The most important features controlling all weathering
have undoubtedly been the joints within the granite. Where
these happened to be closely spaced erosion has been thorough,
forming the basins and depressions of the moor. Where the
joints are more widely spaced the task has been harder and
these areas, the tors and ridges, remain the prominent features
of the moor today.

MAP 7

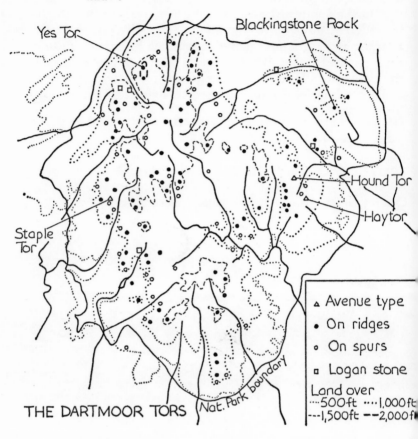

THE DARTMOOR TORS

Yes Tor

Blackingstone Rock

Hound Tor

Haytor

Staple Tor

Nat. Park boundary

△ Avenue type
● On ridges
○ On spurs
□ Logan stone

Land over
····500ft ····1,000ft
---1,500ft --2,000ft

In addition, weathering at individual sites has also been controlled by the elevation, exposure and aspect and by the nature of the existing slopes around them. Take Sharpitor and Leather Tors for examples. Their northern faces are far more shattered than their southern ones, and massive clitters are easily produced because both overlook steep slopes on the north side.

For these reasons Dartmoor tors cannot be classified, they are too individualistic, but they can be broadly grouped. Anyone who has visited a number of them will have sorted them into two major groups, tors which mark the end of a projecting spur and tors which occur roughly in rows along the major ridges of the moor, (Map 7). Those who live in

Devon especially, and others able to spend several holidays there, can enjoy a long series of excursions 'tor collecting'.

The feature common to all of them is the rounded nature of the higher blocks. Mechanical and chemical weathering are most successful in areas nearest the surface. Both work in the joints, rounding and discolouring the blocks. Mechanical methods have already been described in Chapter 4.

Chemical weathering distinguishes between the quartz, felspars and mica. The black mica or biotite is oxidised and the felspars are converted to clay minerals and carbonates. Quartz survives best under chemical attack and so it forms the bulk of the weathered residue, often found in little mounds where vertical joints reach ground level at the base of a tor. The lower areas of tors tend to be more angular; weathering is obviously less successful farther from the surface.

FIG 12

THE ORIGIN OF TORS

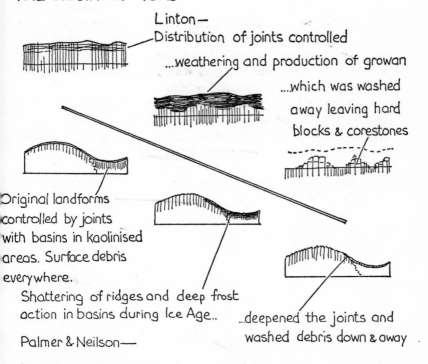

Linton —
Distribution of joints controlled

...weathering and production of growan

...which was washed away leaving hard blocks & corestones

Original landforms controlled by joints with basins in kaolinised areas. Surface debris everywhere.

Shattering of ridges and deep frost action in basins during Ice Age..

..deepened the joints and washed debris down & away

Palmer & Neilson—

D

THE ORIGIN OF THE TORS

Previous theories have taken up directly opposed positions above the origin of the tors, (Figure 12). In 1955, D. L. Linton favoured chemical weathering by ground water circulating through the joints. The blocks which remained, either through sheer size or because they were more physically resistant, were called 'corestones' .The corestones were let down upon each other by the mechanical removal of the waste around them and so formed the tors. Corestones are not easily found on Dartmoor, however, Great Staple, Hound, and Great Mis tors probably provide the most convincing examples.

In 1962 Palmer and Neilson suggested the opposite, an entirely mechanical origin. The tors were left behind when all the rock around them was broken up and removed by frost action, and the rounding of the blocks must therefore be normal atmospheric weathering, occurring since the Ice Age.

Looking at Dartmoor tors it is difficult to attribute them mainly to either cause. They must be the product of a combination of processes, and while the effects are obvious no one can yet say which type of weathering was mainly responsible. Frost action has played the most recent part, but it may well have attacked tors which were already in existence and of previous chemical origin.

One major problem is the fact that we do not know what the original upper surface of the granite looked like. Did its irregularities determine the surface of the granite today? Erosion has certainly not penetrated more than 50-200 metres into the mass.

Perhaps we are concentrating too much on the tors in studying the Dartmoor landscape. The chemical weathering by circulating groundwater which Linton suggested would surely have sought out existing depressions and attacked the basins of the moor rather than the tors. Chemical weathering would be very successful in these more closely jointed basins.

In Oligocene times, weathered products of the Dartmoor surface formed the ball clays of Petrockstow and the Bovey Basin. Similar products must have left the moor along its other valleys, but they were deposited further afield, beyond the present coastline. The tors would be opened up along their joints at the same time as the chemical attack on the basins,

ready to suffer the maximum of mechanical damage in the
the Ice Age. The Ice Age could also have completed the
removal of chemically weathered material from the basins.

Two things are certain—that the tors are residual features,

FIG 13

BOWERMAN'S NOSE 74280 4 NW
Easdon Tor

Strong 'east-west' and 'north-south' vertical joints form
21·5 ft high pile

relics left behind in the general destruction of the moorland
surface, and that they are not the work of the Druids as was
once suggested !

The tors stand then as residual piles, surviving for the time
being the destructive agents at work around them, offering
one of the finest therapies available today to those who spend
a quiet hour or two on one. They are sentinels in a landscape
held in a delicate balance between the rate of production of
weathered debris on the one hand and the rate of its removal
on the other. Map 7 shows the distribution of the more im-

portant tors and indicates some of the features the geologist can study on them, (Figure 7). Rock basins are also illustrated in Figure 34 and described on page 95. For rock shelters see Haytor, page 94, and for logan stones see Black Tor, page 85.

CHAPTER 6

West Dartmoor

Tavy Cleave is an isolated spot now, but man once made greater use of the area. There are groups of hut circles around the cleave itself, and further up the Rattlebrook a peatworks operated in the nineteenth century. Visiting the cleave is unfortunately limited to days when there is no firing on the near-by army ranges.

FIG 14

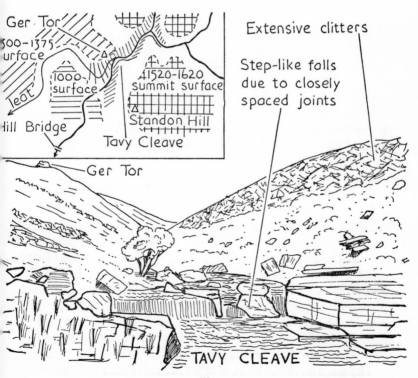

TAVY CLEAVE

FIG 15

WIDTH OF METAMORPHIC AUREOLE OUTCROP

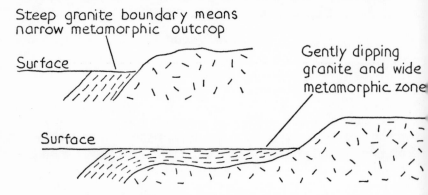

Steep granite boundary means narrow metamorphic outcrop

Surface

Gently dipping granite and wide metamorphic zone

Surface

In this spectacular section of its valley the Tavy drops nearly 300ft through a two-mile cleft in the granite south of Hare Tor. The valley sides are clitter-strewn, with crags on the northern slope. Tavy Cleave illustrates the close relationship of a river and the natural joints in granite. It has excavated this gorge because the horizontal and vertical joints are closely spaced here. In the bottom of the valley, the solid granite forms squarish blocks with numerous step-like waterfalls and short intervening pools. What contrast this granite gorge makes with the one cut in Culm Measures at Lydford !

There are several remnants of the higher Dartmoor erosion surfaces on the hillsides above the cleave (Figure 14). The Tavy leaves the gorge at 1,000ft above sea level and remnants of this surface appear along the valley side below, towards Kingsett Down. The leat flowing from the cleave formerly crossed the down to provide extra waterpower for Wheal Betsy mine but the road back to Mary Tavy keeps further to the east. It passes over Horndon Down Common where there are plenty of exposures of volcanic dolerite, or greenstone. The weathered outer surfaces appear deceptively like granite at a first glance. The dolerites are very hard but once a piece has been chipped off the crystalline green colour can be seen.

The dolerite intrusions cover an extensive area around Mary

Tavy and Peter Tavy and appear to the south in Cox Tor and in sills at Pitts Cleave quarries, near Tavistock. They were formed and folded with the Carboniferous rocks which surround them, and to the east of the Tavy villages they were altered again by the heat released from the granite on its arrival. Important mineral lodes were formed around Mary Tavy at this time and reference to Sheet 338 of the Geological Survey map shows how the metamorphic zone is very wide in the Mary Tavy area. Figure 15 reveals how this is evidence of a very gentle dip below ground along the granite boundary.

THE MARY TAVY MINES

The chief mine in the parish was Devon Friendship. The site straddles the Cholwell Brook where the lane leading to the parish church crosses the valley. West of the stream, the dumps are stained with green oxidised copper—green copper

FIG 16

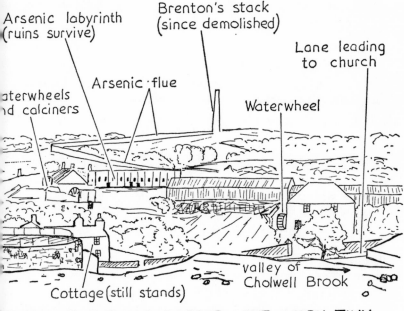

Arsenic labyrinth (ruins survive)

Brenton's stack (since demolished)

Lane leading to church

Arsenic flue

aterwheels nd calciners

Waterwheel

valley of Cholwell Brook

Cottage(still stands)

DEVON FRIENDSHIP COPPER MINE MARY TAVY
N 1904   505794 NE

ore is known as malachite. Broken pieces will reveal the 'fool's gold' ore, chalcopyrite, and grey lead ores may be found as well, since both the lode and the workings of Wheal Betsy, higher up the brook, continued down into Devon Friendship.

From its group of E-W lodes Devon Friendship produced an estimated 155,089 tons of copper and 13,380 tons of secondary arsenic between 1800 and 1885. The lodes cross the A386 road to the west as well, but the main working area was always the eastern part of the mine and its life extended from at least 1796 to 1924. Mary Tavy is the classic example of the difference between the trend of tin and copper lodes (E-W) and that of lead and silver lodes (N-S), for north of the village lies Wheal Betsy. The well-known engine-house is a familiar landmark below the Black Down road. A line of old shafts follows the Cholwell Brook, and although the dumps have been picked over and re-smelted, galena (lead sulphide) specimens can be found near the bridge leading to Cholwell farm. The best way to find them is to break open lumps of quartz vein, preferably thinner veined pieces; ordinary rock waste or large white quartz vein is less rewarding. The northernmost shafts of the mine are across the A386 road in Henscott plantations.

Wheal Betsy produced 80.5 per cent and 73 per cent ores, yielding nine ounces of silver from each ton of lead. Its recorded silver production exceeds 8,000 ounces and its annual lead output reached 400-500 tons.

BRENTOR

West of Mary Tavy lies Brentor. Crowned by its little church, 1,130ft above the sea, it is a solitary landmark visible from a wide area of west Devon. Like the dolerites at Mary Tavy, Brentor is further evidence that the volcanic activity which had begun in Devonian times continued into the Carboniferous period. But here the product was different because Brentor is formed of pillow lavas, which are the work of underwater eruptions, the lava breaking away in lumps which fall to the deeper areas of the sea bed. There, still partly liquid, they accumulate just like a jumbled heap of pillows. The best pillow lavas seen in south Devon are at Chipley, near Newton Abbot (*Geology Explained in South and East Devon,* p 178). At Brentor, exposures are limited to the base of the knoll, partly because the lavas here have been rotted and also because of the intense folding they suffered at the close of Carboniferous times.

FIG 17

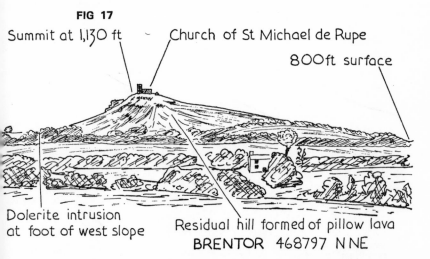

Summit at 1,130 ft ‒ Church of St Michael de Rupe

800ft surface

Dolerite intrusion at foot of west slope

Residual hill formed of pillow lava
BRENTOR 468797 NNE

Although it is built of lava 200ft thick, the resemblance of Brentor to a volcano is, in fact, a coincidence. Its shape is the accidental result of erosion. Originally part of a hill summit at the 1,000ft level, it was all but trimmed away when the next surface was formed at 800ft. The 800ft level still exists in a broad area north-west of the hill, extending beyond Lydford Gorge to Longham, Galford and Burley Downs. The northern limit overlooks the valley of the river Lew.

In clear weather Brentor is an ideal spot at which to sit with a geological map and work out on a grand scale the links between rock types and scenery. Away to the east is the distinctive change of slope which marks the outer face of Dartmoor. Metamorphosed Carboniferous rocks form the whole of its slopes, extending beyond the summits of White Tor and Cox Tor. These altered slates also border the granite at Sourton Tors whose profile can be seen to the north-west.

To the north, the plateau-like ridge tops of mid-Devon form an unbroken vista, bevelled by the 690ft and lower erosion surfaces. Bodmin Moor appears near at hand to the west, although it is actually sixteen miles from Dartmoor. The

MAP 8

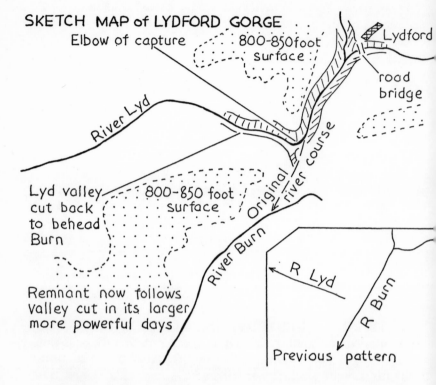

SKETCH MAP of LYDFORD GORGE

Elbow of capture

800-850 foot surface

Lydford

road bridge

River Lyd

Original river course

Lyd valley cut back to behead Burn

800-850 foot surface

River Burn

Remnant now follows valley cut in its larger more powerful days

R Lyd

R Burn

Previous pattern

prominent steep margin of the Bodmin granite overlooking the river Lynher is easily picked out. The intervening country, the heavily mineralised district of the Tamar valley, is too low to be seen from Brentor for the river cuts very deeply through that district.

The Tamar is not the only river to remain hidden from this vantage point. North of Brentor, a twisting line of woodland marks the deep cut of the river Lyd.

LYDFORD GORGE

Lydford has a rich history—decayed borough, parochial centre of Dartmoor, and site of the ill-reputed stannary prison in its grim castle. Long since surpassed by its nearest rival markets at Tavistock and Okehampton, its chief attraction to tourists now is the remarkable gorge. Though famous among

Devon gorges, Lydford's claims do not rest on physical size so much as on the deep, awe-inspiring plunge beneath Lydford Bridge and the beauty of the woodlands and waterfalls in the lower sections.

Many Devon gorges are associated with the granite margin but Lydford even lies beyond the metamorphic aureole. The 150ft cleft is walled by slates of Upper Devonian age, involved at a later date in complex folding. Often the only clue to folds are the group of lenticles within the slates, but the narrowness of the gorge usually prevents one standing back far enough to see the details.

The gorge, National Trust property, is open only in the summer months and should be entered near the Manor House Inn at the lower end. Here the explorer can find the key to its existence. A glance at the map reveals the general south-

FIG 18

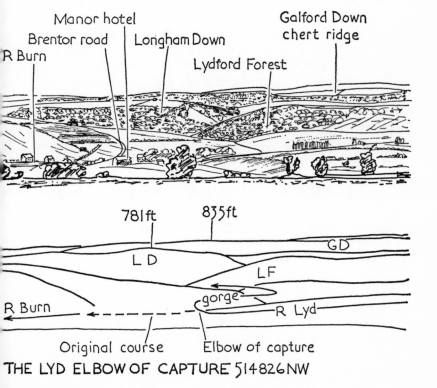

THE LYD ELBOW OF CAPTURE 514826 NW

west direction of the river Lyd and the river Tavy. Yet just before it reaches the old Lydford Junction station, the river Lyd suddenly turns off to the north-west. This sharp bend marks the site of a river-capture and is termed the 'elbow of capture'.

Map 8 shows how the river Burn was part of the original south-west stream. The Lyd, with a steeper, more powerful course to the river Tamar near Lifton, was able to enlarge its valley upstream. Eventually it broke into the Burn Valley, capturing its upper reaches and leaving the lower Burn as a beheaded remnant. Once it had obtained its prize, the river Lyd set about deepening the upper valley to its own level and Lydford Gorge represents its achievements to date. It will be gradually extended and deepened upstream.

Some of the smaller tributaries along the edge of the gorge, lacking the power of the main stream, have been unable to keep pace. Their entrances high up on the sidewalls are now marked by sheer waterfalls, like the White Lady Fall near the first footbridge above the entrance.

Walking upstream beyond Ravens' Tor tunnel, it is worth keeping an eye on the ground, for just over thirty yards beyond the tunnel thin bands of siltstone outline a fold in the pathway. Along the stream-bed there are countless examples of potholes and their fragments. This attractive woodland walk ends at the second footbridge and beyond it is the narrowest part of the gorge, a sheer plunge formed of huge potholes, the path too steep and fearful for some to venture along it. Generally it is much easier to walk up it than to try to come down.

This cleft below the road bridge is one of the best places in Devon to see how a youthful river sets about deepening its bed. Small hollows in the rock bed have become the centres of eddies where the water swirls around the stones it carries. Eventually deepening, the hollow bores down into the stream bed forming a solid pothole. The depth of potholes is only limited by the power of the stream to rotate the pebbles trapped in the bottom. Progress is next made by widening neighbouring potholes until all the intervening walls are removed. A new level has then been achieved and the process can begin again.

In this upper reach of the gorge there is one enormous

example, the Devil's Cauldron. The walls above it are sculptured with the alcove-like fragments of earlier series.

There have been many other river captures in Devon apart from the river Lyd—between the Walkham and the upper Blackbrook or the Mole and the Taw, for example. The sharp change of direction at the elbow and the beheaded valley beyond are obvious clues. An amusing half hour can be spent with map and ruler working out how an extension of this valley could have linked up with that one—but beware of hasty conclusions!

WHITCHURCH COMMON

Whitchurch Common forms an impressive level running southwards from the Tavistock-Princetown road to Pew Tor, where quarrying was active in the ninteenth century. The common is part of the 1,050-1,350ft surface, formed under land conditions after the tilting of the Dartmoor upland. A fine tour can be made starting from the car park at the top of Pork Hill, and arriving here from the Princetown direction the change of scene is so sudden at this point that it is very easy to commit oneself to going down Pork Hill before the car park can be gained. The transformation from the level granite common to the steep metamorphosed slopes and then to the extensive remains of the 690ft surface at their base is amazing.

The cross-roads at Moorshop can be seen at the bottom of the hill and marks the probable junction of Devonian and Carboniferous beds west of the moor. The 690ft level cuts regardless across both groups, a fact often quoted as evidence of its marine origin. But since the beds on either side are similar in nature there is no reason for the surface to make any difference between them. It can be traced away to the south-west, forming the site of Whitchurch Common (golf course), Plaster Down (army camp), and towards Plymouth can be seen undulating across Roborough Down where slight rises in its level are caused by east-west felsite dykes. Between Yelverton and Plymouth, its old shore-line lies east of the river Meavy.

If the weather is clear the distinctive waste dumps of the

MAP 9

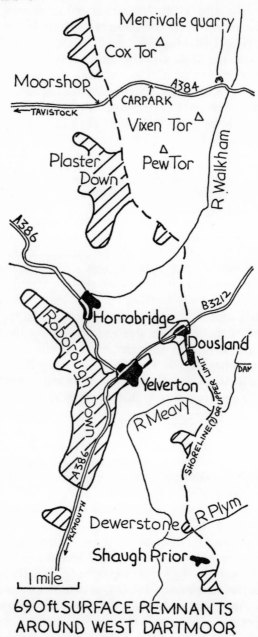

690ft SURFACE REMNANTS
AROUND WEST DARTMOOR

St Austell claypits can be seen far to the west before the walker sets off for the north side of the common.

Just as an artist stands back to inspect his canvas, so are many Dartmoor features more deeply understood by a distant view rather than by close inspection. Some times of year are better than others—in summer, bracken hides the details of the clitters. Other features vary with the light quality, and the long evening shadows often pick out small objects which were hidden at mid-day. Thus Cox Tor and the Staple Tor act as vantage points for each other.

FIG 19

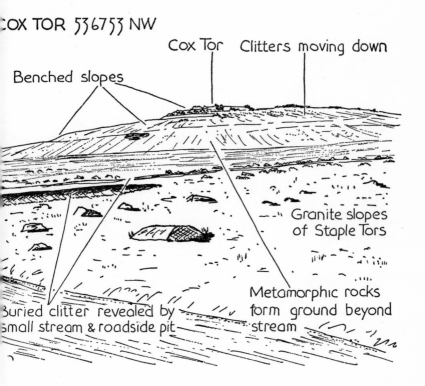

COX TOR 536753 NW

Cox Tor   Clitters moving down

Benched slopes

Granite slopes of Staple Tors

Metamorphic rocks form ground beyond stream

Buried clitter revealed by small stream & roadside pit

Climbing northwards from the car park, there is a good scramble up the slopes of Cox Tor. The tor lies centrally in the metamorphic zone, its bench-like slopes the work of frost action on its altered slates and dolerites. Where these beds were visible, frost action kept their faces rough and nearly vertical. Probably there was spring-sapping, too, the process by which water undermines rocks as it emerges at their base. Falls result, but fragments are soon carried away by the stream and a natural quarry face is set up, working its way deeper into the hillside. Other moorland sites with benched slopes include Smeardon Down (Peter Tavy), Sourton Tors and East Hill, Brent Hill (South Brent) and Black Hill above Becky Falls.

The small valley between Cox Tor and the Staple Tors ridge has been cut along the junction of metamorphic zone and granite. From its slopes there is a good view of the Cox Tor benches on the one hand and the patterned clitter on Great and Middle Staple Tors on the other.

Climbing up to Staple Tors the patterning becomes very noticeable, between intervals of easy turf walking there are strips of large blocks running down-slope. Their net-like arrangement is the work of frost heaving. The normal expansion of water on freezing is powerful enough to turn over quite large boulders and pile them in small ridges. This recalls the old gardening maxim to let the frost break up the soil, and every lawn expert knows he has to roll the lumps down again in the spring!

The size of Great Staple Tor may be due to the tourmaline veins which fill its joints, making destruction more difficult. However, it has still lost most of its central blocks by frost heaving. When the centre of a tor is removed in this way it is termed an 'avenue' type. Haytor, described in Chapter 9, is a fine example.

From Staple Tors, walk south-east to Merrivale Quarry, described in Chapter 10, and complete the tour of Whitchurch Common with a visit to Vixen Tor. Its unusual position in the Walkham valley is deceiving for the sphinx-like pile is actually the highest on Dartmoor, 93ft on its southern side.

BURRATOR

Most people appreciate the scenic qualities of Burrator. (Figure 20). Constructed in 1893-8 and extended in 1928, the reservoir submerged a gorge cut by the river Meavy just within the granite boundary. The secondary dam towards Sheepstor village caused problems at the time because the granite there

FIG 20

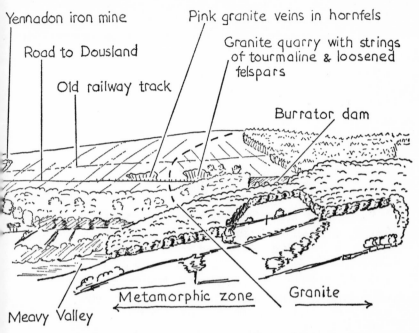

Yennadon iron mine

Road to Dousland

Old railway track

Pink granite veins in hornfels

Granite quarry with strings of tourmaline & loosened felspars

Burrator dam

Metamorphic zone

Granite

Meavy Valley

THE GRANITE BOUNDARY AT BURRATOR 554666 NNW

was deeply rotted. An excavation 100ft deep was necessary to secure a watertight structure.

The original dam was largely constructed with granite taken from a quarry just inside the reservoir area, on the Sheepstor side. Although this site is now submerged, other quarries worked during the later heightening reveal the nature of the granite and its contact with the metamorphic rocks along the road to Dousland. The quarry nearest the dam contains a few large felspars, enough to class it as feebly porphyritic, but it is more interesting for its tourmalinisation. Thin black lines or 'stringers' of the mineral can be traced upwards, causing a reddening of the joint planes in the granite. Away from the joints, the reddening decreases and in their central areas the blocks of granite are unaffected.

Other interesting examples of chemical rotting occur, and close inspection reveals rectangular cavities where felspar

E

crystals have been removed. Some can be seen still in position but loosened by the partial destruction of their rims.

Further south in the next quarry it is even more exciting, for here one of the finest exposures of the granite contact can be studied. Veins of pinkish granite can be traced both vertically and horizontally through the metamorphosed beds of Upper Devonian slate. Known as 'hornfels', these heated slates are rich in cordierite—a blue-grey mineral often associated with slates altered by high temperatures. The slates are dark, spotted rocks now, but traces of their original sedimentary bedding are still visible.

PEEK HILL

Some most attractive walks can be made through the forestry plantations around Burrator. Explorers should keep to the well-marked tracks and strict fire precautions must always be observed. From the upper road on the north side make for Leather Tor. The going is steep at first but the tor offers fine views, and extensive clitters have formed below its northern face and also on near-by Sharpitor.

From Sharpitor, a circular tour can be completed by turning south-west down the slopes of Peek Hill to the B3212 and then by lanes over the ridge again to Burrator. The slopes of Peek Hill will occupy the walker for some time. Every small boulder here reveals altered spilites. They are quite hard, but specimens show these are black rocks, very like flint, with greenish bands of hornblende and pyroxene. White bands of quartz also occur.

CHAPTER 7

Lee Moor and China Clay

The landscape so common around the Westcountry clay
pits is a rare scene by world standards. The china-clay deposits
of Devon and Cornwall are among the largest and richest
yet discovered, and as sources of this clay are few it forms
one of Britain's most valuable exports. It is the cheapest and
purest inert filler available today and to meet the demanding
specifications of modern technology its production must be
skilfully controlled.

Kaolin, or china clay, was known, named and used by the
Chinese long before its products were introduced into Europe
in the sixteenth century. Before then, household products
were usually made of pewter and wood. The discovery of this
remarkable material in the Westcountry was the work of a
Kingsbridge man, William Cookworthy. A chemist, with a
shop in Notte Street, Plymouth, he found it first in Cornwall
in 1748. About 1768 he started a china factory in Plymouth
which was later moved to Bristol.

Devon and Cornwall are ideal for the industry. Most of the
pits lie between 700 and 1,000ft above the sea, giving good
downhill flow for pipelines supplying wet clay slurry to drying works nearer the coast. The moorlands provide plenty of
fresh, clear water for the traditional method of washing out
the deposits. Since most of the granite districts are nearer the
south coast with its better harbours and large estuaries, sea
transport is usually close at hand.

Map 10 shows the kaolinised areas of the Dartmoor granite
and the areas of present and former clay works. In most of
the disused works the deposits were very shallow, little more
than the accumulation of clay washed out of very mildly
kaolinised granite on the slopes nearby. The best areas are
undoubtedly those on the south-west margin where present-
day expansion is so rapid.

MAP 10

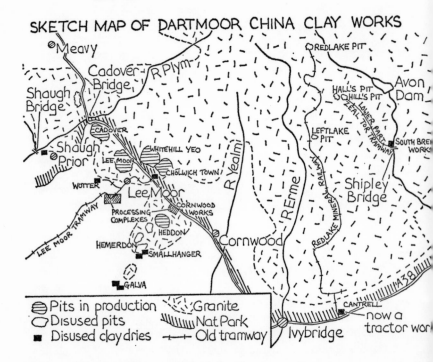

SKETCH MAP OF DARTMOOR CHINA CLAY WORKS

⊖ Pits in production
◯ Disused pits
■ Disused clay dries
✕ Granite
Nat Park
┼┼ Old tramway

Here the altered zone trends NW-SE along the granite margin from Cadover Bridge to Heddon Down, a direction shared by the fault which cuts through this part of Dartmoor (see Map 11.) The alignment is only coincidence, however, for the kaolinisation followed the arrival of the granite whereas the fault is a much younger Tertiary tear-fault running between Tavistock and Modbury. In fact, in the Lee Moor Pit kaolinisation is most intense in a north-south direction, particularly where east-west quartz- tourmaline dykes are crossed.

The south-west Dartmoor kaolin deposits are a classic example of the deep alteration which occurred in the granite because the decomposition originated from below. The solutions were able to work their way up, rotting the felspars in widening bodies. These can be pictured as elongated funnel shapes.

The Lee Moor works on Dartmoor were opened in 1830 and developed from 1833 by William Phillips and then by

Martin Brothers from 1862. As well as clay products, bricks and salt-glaze sanitary ware were made and over many parts of the district the name 'Martin Bros', can be seen on old walls. The frequency with which the name is seen is a measure of the expansion which took place at Lee Moor in the latter half of the nineteenth century. The works are still expanding rapidly under their present-day owners, English China Clays Ltd.

For those who have never previously visited china-clay pits, the variety of veins present may be an unexpected feature. Veins of tourmaline, amethyst and other minerals are frequently found in normal granite exposures and in the altered zones they were unaffected by the decomposition which went on around them.

THE LANDSCAPE OF THE CLAYWORKS

Lee Moor and Crownhill Down provide the tourist with a foretaste of Cornwall, a smaller version of areas like the Hensbarrow granite outcrop north of St Austell. Seen from

FIG 21

THE CHINA CLAY DISTRICT 561604N

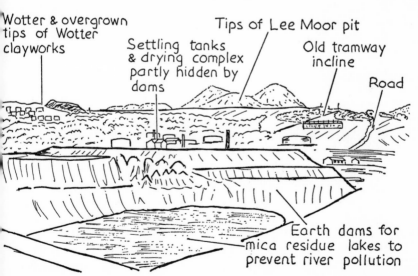

Wotter & overgrown tips of Wotter clayworks

Tips of Lee Moor pit

Settling tanks & drying complex partly hidden by dams

Old tramway incline

Road

Earth dams for mica residue lakes to prevent river pollution

afar, the landscape is dominated by the huge, tent-like waste tips. Constructed from steep inclines leading up over the sides of the pits, they contain the unwanted quartz sand and mica. This sparkling crystalline material remains bare of plant life for tens of years after it has been dumped. Incidentally, rainwater gullying and furrowing the loose slopes provides the geologist with excellent outdoor models of river valley development.

China-clay waste tips are not in the same class as other industrial waste tips, however. Certainly they are an inescapable intrusion into the landscape, but at least they are clean. They do not bring the problem of constant slow burning which affects coal-mine tips, nor are they as unstable as their loose slopes would suggest. The sand waste, being coarse-grained, adjusts itself to a reasonable slope as soon as it is dumped while the extremely porous nature of the material means there is good internal drainage. The sort of landslip which occurs in the East Devon cliffs, when the underlying marl surfaces become saturated after heavy rainfall, is an unlikely event on one of these gigantic mounds.

Tips have seldom been moved deliberately except where, in the early days, low sale prices meant building them as near the pit as possible to save cost. Good clay ground was sometimes buried beneath them. The size of modern tips shows how their modern use for building sand, reformite blocks and calcium silicate bricks has only just begun to deal with the industry's extensive waste disposal problem. As sources of sand and gravel in other areas of southern England become more scarce, greater use will certainly be made of the stocks around West Country claypits.

At Lee Moor the most recent aid to waste disposal is the highly modernised calcium silicate brick plant commissioned in 1966. Now using 2,000 tons of waste sand per week, it is facing a growing demand for this product.

The shape of claypits is not always related to the areas altered to china clay, sometimes because the alteration was patchy or locally incomplete. Historical factors, such as landowners' boundaries or the small areas granted in old leases, may also be relevant. So a simple relationship of pit areas to the extent of the clay deposits would be misleading.

At Lee Moor, working has previously been limited for

amenity reasons, the deposits straddling the boundary of the Dartmoor National Park. In 1958 permission was refused for extensions on the high ground near Shell Top, beyond the head of Tory brook. Collard Tor above Wotter, and land between it and Hawks Tor, were also excluded from the developments. About 850 acres of workings were left inside the National Park boundary, mainly the Whitehill Yeo and Cholwich Town pits north of the Cadover Bridge to Cornwood road. Present production plans to cover the next fifty years will require permission for a huge pit in this area. Two and a half miles long, one mile wide and of unknown depth, it would eventually become a lake for amenity purposes.

Another limiting factor is the safety measure which decrees that pits may not be worked within 100ft of a road. This is a precaution against landslips since no limit to the depth of the deposits seems to have been reached yet and pits are already working at depths of over 350ft. The china-clay bodies are thick because, as mentioned above, the chemical alteration which produced them originated deep down rather than from the surface of the moor. Since the felspars affected by this special kind of decomposition occur only in granite, the distribution of china-clay resources is bound to be fairly limited. Absence of discolouring iron minerals is another im-

FIG 22

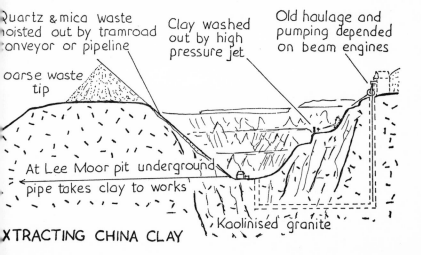

Quartz & mica waste hoisted out by tramroad conveyor or pipeline

Clay washed out by high pressure jet

Old haulage and pumping depended on beam engines

Coarse waste tip

At Lee Moor pit underground pipe takes clay to works

Kaolinised granite

XTRACTING CHINA CLAY

portant factor, because commercially the whiteness of the clay is essential.

WINNING THE CLAY

The whole process of clay excavation and refining depends on water. At Lee Moor, the Tory brook supply is augmented by a leat from the river Plym. Abandoned pits may also form useful reservoirs and in most clayworks much of the water used is re-circulated.

High-pressure water monitors delivering 1,500 gallons a minute spray the pit-face, dislodging the material which then runs away across the pit floor. If there are any slightly stained areas visible on the face, the water is only sprayed on them at intervals. The discoloured clay is thus gradually blended with the purer and the quality of the clay stream maintained.

The coarse sand, quartz and mica minerals, settles out of the stream in the pit bottom and travels up to the waste tip high above by hoist, conveyor belt or pipeline. Formerly, waste tips were supplied by cable-powered railways carrying self-emptying hopper wagons and driven by engine-houses standing on the far side of the tip from the claypit itself. Before that, when hand or horse-drawn tramways were used, tips were long and low in shape.

Twelve per cent of the clay rock is extracted as clay, and since production on Dartmoor is now 8,000 tons of clay per week from Lee Moor alone, the size of the waste problem can readily be appreciated. The clay stream leaves the pit by pumping, or in some cases through an adit driven from a near-by valley, eg, Lee Moor Pit.

INDUSTRIAL ARCHAEOLOGY OF THE CLAY INDUSTRY

Any clayworks looks somewhat chaotic and the methods perhaps old-fashioned, but this is deceptive. If necessary, china clay can be washed and dried ready for sale less than twenty-four hours after it has been removed from the ground, and the industry is constantly improving its science and efficiency.

The second stage in processing the clay stream is to trap and remove the flaky mica which remains. The old mica-traps, or 'drags', are one of the distinctive remains found on clayworking sites which can otherwise present quite a problem to industrial archaeologists. Little more than a maze of overgrown banks and channels is usually visible among the dumps, with perhaps a ruined kiln here and there.

FIG 23

OLD MICA TRAPS at STOCKERS PIT HEMERDON
Built in concrete about 1923

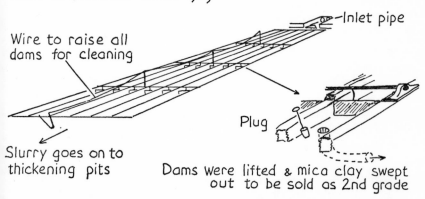

Inlet pipe

Wire to raise all dams for cleaning

Slurry goes on to thickening pits

Plug

Dams were lifted & mica clay swept out to be sold as 2nd grade

The 'micas' or 'drags' worked simply by slowing down the clay stream so that the flaky pieces were precipitated out in the bottom of a series of channels. The earlier types had increasing numbers of channels, usually in a 1-2-4 pattern. Later, 'micas' were built with the same number of channels throughout but of much greater length, up to 300ft. In both cases wooden dams (the drags) spanned the channels at regular intervals. These dams could be adjusted to vary the amount of mica trapped and, in fact, only the coarsest deposits were rejected completely. The finer material was marketed as second-grade clay while the whole water stream from the 'micas' went through the system a second time. Near the wooden dams were plug-holes down which the unwanted mica was washed at intervals of a few hours. Clay workers swept the material down the channels with a 'shiver', a rake-like implement made of wood.

After the 'micas', the clay stream goes to catch-pits where it is slowly stirred and thickened by draining off as much water as possible. The old thickening pits had a distinctive row of vertical holes up one side. As the clay slurry settled and the top water cleared, so the plugs were removed from these holes one by one and the surplus water on top allowed to run away.

In the old days the clay was dug from the pits by hand and taken in barrows to the drying sheds nearby. Natural air drying was the oldest method, taking weeks to complete, especially in winter. Blocks of clay were placed on shelves in open-sided sheds. Many potters preferred this air-dried clay to the kiln-dried, but it was a slow method which could only survive in days when production and demand were small. An old air-drying shed still stands at Smallhanger works on Crownhill Down (see below).

FIG 24

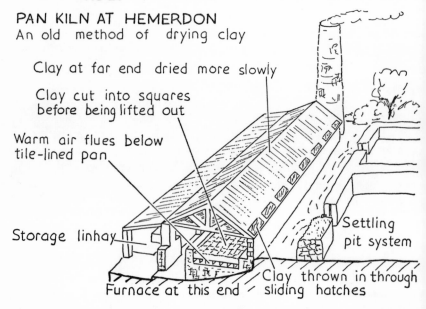

PAN KILN AT HEMERDON
An old method of drying clay

Clay at far end dried more slowly

Clay cut into squares before being lifted out

Warm air flues below tile-lined pan

Storage linhay

Furnace at this end

Clay thrown in through sliding hatches

Settling pit system

Then came the pan kiln, a shallow tile-lined tank about 18in deep, 12ft wide and often over 100ft long, with warm air passing through ducts beneath the floor. The tiles used for the floor were made locally from quartz waste and were often thickest, and the pan at its deepest, at the furnace end of the building where the drying out was quicker. A chimney stood at the opposite end to the firing hearth, the white plume of smoke coming from it theoretically containing all the moisture from the clay drawn through the porous tile floor. Those who worked in the dries knew better !

Until recently, many of these old clay dries could be seen in the district, in various stages of ruin. One stood near Tolchmoor Gate until 1969 and there are others below Lee Moor village. An intact example with its storage linhay stands at Galva, near Hemerdon, and there are partly ruined dries at Wotter and Shaugh Bridge.

SMALLHANGER WORKS

The Galva pan kiln is one of two which were built at that site to serve the Smallhanger Clayworks when it opened in 1861. Only the chimney and the foundations of the second kiln remain since it was demolished in 1961.

Smallhanger was typical of the older clay workings, and, since it lies away from the centre of the present activity at Lee Moor and is in better visual shape than most of the other old workings on Dartmoor, it ought to be described briefly.

There were, of course, no monitors, all the washing out being done by diverting streams of water down over the pit faces. The depth of the pits was therefore limited by the slope of the hillside because natural flow out of the pit was also required. In the early days the waste was trammed out of the pits by donkey and cart.

At a later date the works had a waterwheel, winding from the far side of the tips. Its site is now buried in waste. The wheel was never much use for the sett suffered from a general lack of water, as reference to its site on present maps will easily confirm. For much of the time hand-tramming had to be resorted to.

The overburden in the Smallhanger works was 3-4ft deep but on the opposite side of the stream, Hemerdon clayworks had an overburden of 6-7ft. The sand dumps at both sites are little indication of the amount of working now, however, for a great deal of sand was sold off in the building boom of the 1920s.

The mica traps at the works are now very overgrown and buried in clay waste, but higher up the moor, near Stockers Tip, the traps shown in Figure 23 can be found. They are relatively modern traps, built of concrete in 1923.

Much of the drying at Smallhanger was done by air. The old shed has already been mentioned above but it only replaced some older sheds in 1923. Long before there were any sheds at all drying was done in an open sandpit. Women were employed to scrape the sand off the dried blocks, which were then stock-piled on planks under portable roofs of thatch. Later, the floor of the drying pit was paved.

When the sheds came into use the blocks were stacked 4-5 rows high, wet and dry layers alternatively, the latter helping to absorb the moisture of the others. The lumps always had to be lifted by spades since the clay was not stiff enough for the prodder used in the ball clay trade. Both spades and barrows had to be dusted with dry clay to prevent the squarish lumps from sticking to them.

The clay was sent out by horse and cart to Plympton station, bound for the Staffordshire potteries where air-dried clay was valued for its even texture. To maintain regular output, it was therefore necessary to have large dries capable of holding enough clay in the autumn to carry the works through until the spring.

The annual pattern of activity which resulted was : Winter —plenty of water about, washing out. Spring—thickening and starting to dry. Summer—drying and stockpiling for early winter. Autumn—ready to meet a sudden upsurge in sales which the potters always said was due to the extra demand for heavy basins for Christmas puddings! So much for the days before Christmas puddings, too, were mass-produced.

Nowadays modern clayworks speed up the whole process by an additional technique between the catch pit and drying kilns. Filter presses are used to squeeze out the remaining water. The presses are rather like gigantic clothing rails, great square plates covered with nylon filter cloths hang from them. The clay is pumped into the hollows between and the whole rail is then squeezed up, pressing out the water. About 70 per cent of the product of these presses is clay compared to only 30-40 per cent clay if the material is taken direct from the thickening pits.

A variety of drying methods are available in a modern works. Buell and rotary kilns are the most common. The former is a huge vertical cylinder up which a stream of hot air is blown. The clay enters at the top and falls through a series of slotted revolving trays which are swept by stationary arms. By the time it reaches the bottom it is dry and ready for packing. The finest clay of all, however, is obtained by spray-drying, a process comparable to the method of drying milk. A fine spray enters the top of a cylinder and by the time it has floated to the bottom in the warm air current it has changed to a fine powder.

MARKETING AND USING CHINA CLAY

China clay is sold in several standard forms : as a powder, in lumps or pellets, spray-dried, or as a slurry. The powders are divided into divided grades : A and B for paper, C for brown paper, and D for pottery, for example. Each claypit is known for the particular qualities it produces. At Lee Moor, the Whitehill Yeo and Cholwich Town pits supply grades A and B, and Lee Moor pit itself has grades C and D.

There is one kaolin product, the china-stone or petuntse as the Chinese named it, which does not occur on Dartmoor. A partly altered granite, it has to be quarried and crushed. It is produced from the western side of the Hensbarrow granite, near St Austell, and is used in high-quality pottery.

Horse and cart, traction engine and tramway were all used in the old days to get the clay to the coast. Lee Moor had a notable tramway (described in Helen Harris's *Industrial Archaeology of Dartmoor,* David & Charles, 1968) and many remains of it can still be seen. Today, most of the clay goes by pipeline along the old tramway route to dries at Marsh Mills in Plympton, and from Shaugh Lake another pipeline runs to the Cornwood works. Lorries carry the clay to Plymouth for shipment to the continent, or it may go by rail to Fowey where there are larger vessels waiting for export orders destined for North America. The old tramway with its annual capacity of 70,000 tons would have been hopelessly inadequate today.

Despite its name, the main use of china clay now is in papermaking where it acts as a filler to bond the fibres together. Paper-making requires clean bright clay which will make the paper smooth and opaque and improve its absorption of printing ink. Obviously there must be no trace of grit in clays of this quality since they may form up to 35 per cent of the finished product. China clay is also used as a coating, producing the high gloss for art papers. For coating, an adhesive such as starch or casein must be added.

Although paper is the chief user today it was the Staffordshire potters who gave the first impetus to clay working in the Westcountry. China clay is a refractory clay, it does not deform when fired at a high temperature. In modern earthenware it usually forms about 25 per cent of the china body, mixed with 25 per cent of the highly plastic ball clays for easier working. The rest of the body is ground flint (30 **per** cent) and Cornish china-stone (20 per cent). Spode's original bone china recipe, perfected about 1800, was kaolin $3\frac{1}{2}$ parts, Cornish china-stone 4 parts and bone ash 6 parts. Today, bone china contains about 20 per cent kaolin or china clay, 28 per cent china-stone and 47 per cent bone ash. The high quality of Westcountry-derived china clay explains why it is in such demand for these products and why more than three-quarters of the present output is exported.

The filling property of china clay is also valued in rubber manufacture, plastics and paints. It contributes greatly to medicines, acting as a harmless means of embodying active ingredients in powder and tablet forms. With at least 500 years' reserves known, it is an amazing legacy to us of events which occurred 290 million years ago. Even so, it is a wasting asset and will eventually pass from the Dartmoor landscape

FIG 25

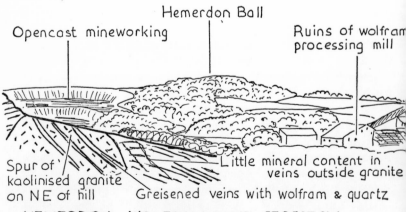

Hemerdon Ball

Opencast mineworking

Ruins of wolfram processing mill

Spur of kaolinised granite on NE of hill

Little mineral content in veins outside granite

Greisened veins with wolfram & quartz

HEMERDON   WOLFRAM   MINE   578597 SW

into history like the days of tin and copper mining. There are several small and now abandoned works which never developed so promisingly as Lee Moor; Brent Moor, Leftlake and Redlake among them.

HEMERDON WOLFRAM

Just south of Lee Moor at Hemerdon Ball is the site of another large opencast industry—the Hemerdon wolfram mine. This mine has worked intermittently since 1917 and may reopen again in the future.

Wolfram or tungsten, a valuable hardening agent in steel manufacture, is an accessory mineral of the tin zone and occurs here in a 2-3ft wide quartz lode and its ramifications. The lode runs NE, following a spur of the granite outcrop across the summit of the hill and eventually becomes such a mass of veins that it is known as a stockworks.

MAP 11

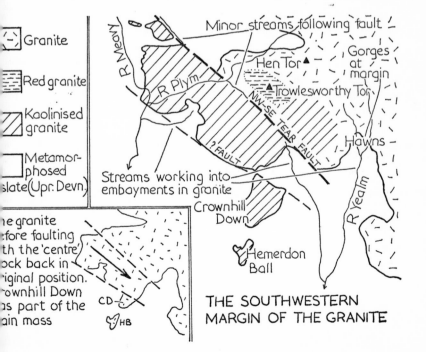

THE SOUTHWESTERN MARGIN OF THE GRANITE

Some shaft mining was undertaken here during the second world war, the supply being augmented by hand-picked wolfram sent over from the Roborough mine, an opencast working on Roborough Down, about half a mile south of Hoo Meavy old railway bridge. Despite the wartime need, the processing mill at Hemerdon never reached its full capacity and now stands in ruins. The mine is still believed to contain 2,500,000 tons of ore and even though it occurs as a very low percentage of the rock bulk, world prices dictate profitability and it could become a paying proposition again. The final chapter in its history has probably not been written; a new survey of its potential was commenced in 1970.

Given permission to enter, the explorer should look for the typical black, lustrous crystals. They are tabular and often diamond-shaped in outline. The good lustre is only present on the cleavage faces, on other fractures the samples are dull. In the opencast working the granite is coarse-grained and, as might be expected so near the clayworking area, kaolinised. Numerous greisened bands run through it. Generally about one foot wide, these bands contain one or two quartz veins each and the wolfram can be found in sporadic bunches along the sides of these veins. Coarse cassiterite occurs in strings near the centre.

Before leaving Hemerdon the explorer should study the Geological Survey one-inch map. It reveals how the Hemerdon Ball granite is detached from the main Dartmoor outcrop, forming an outlier. The boundary of the main granite mass is also interesting. Map 11 shows how its outline was affected by the tear-fault referred to earlier which runs from Tavistock to Modbury. It is one of the group active in mid-Tertiary times with the Sticklepath Fault (Chapter 11).

Chapter 8

Central and Southern Dartmoor

Like the headings of the other regional chapters on Dartmoor, the term 'central and southern' is here based on common usage rather than any definite boundary. Here it includes the districts between Birch Tor, Postbridge and Princetown, and the area of moorland to the south.

TWO BRIDGES QUARRY

FIG 26

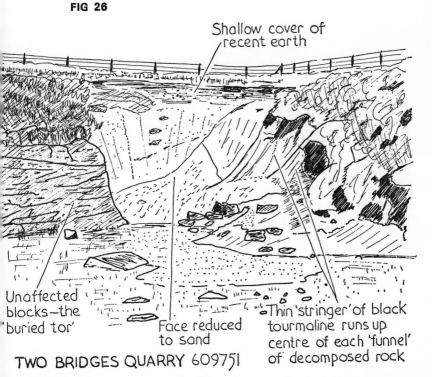

Shallow cover of recent earth

Unaffected blocks—the 'buried tor'

Face reduced to sand

Thin 'stringer' of black tourmaline runs up centre of each 'funnel' of decomposed rock

TWO BRIDGES QUARRY 609751

F

Doubtless, the two major roads across the moor have emphasised the separate geographical identity of southern Dartmoor. Almost on their junction is a little sand quarry which must be one of the best known on Dartmoor, since the National Park information caravan stands there. Large blocks of solid granite can be seen in a mass of decomposed growan, giving the visitor the impression of a buried tor. Fully exposed it would certainly look like one, though it would be one of the rarer valley-side examples.

Similar conditions existed around all the tors at one time, as described in Chapter 5, the combination of chemical and mechanical weathering producing a rock debris which could be removed, leaving only undamaged blocks. But the Two Bridges growan is more than a weathering product; its formation began with chemical changes working upwards from the granite itself.

Studying the deep funnels of growan between the solid blocks, the explorer will discover a thin black line or stringer of tourmaline running up the centre in each case. These confirm that decomposing solutions migrated into the quarry. Destruction began long before the sort of chemical and mechanical destruction associated with the moorland surface had any influence.

THE ROADSIDE PITS OF DARTMOOR

Two Bridges quarry is only one of the many pits which were developed for gravel or small stone supplies along the Dartmoor roadsides. Rotted broken granite was easily obtained a few feet below the peaty soils all over the moor. Many of these pits are now picnic lay-bys and on windy days one with the right aspect can be a boon.

Geologists recognise that important evidence about the later history of Dartmoor is to be found in them. The distribution of soil, growan and glacial Head reveals the effects of the Ice Age on the moorland. In undisturbed conditions the pits would be like that shown at top left on Figure 27 with a zone of growan above the sound granite, grading upwards in turn to peat at the surface. The cold conditions upset this arrangement, mixing the ingredients haphazardly in slumping movements or even reversing the whole sequence by carrying the

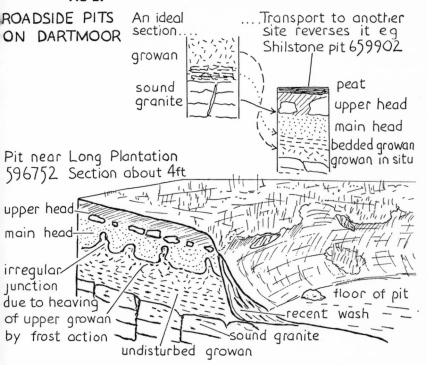

FIG 27

ROADSIDE PITS ON DARTMOOR

An ideal section....

growan

sound granite

....Transport to another site reverses it e g Shilstone pit 659902

peat
upper head
main head
bedded growan
growan in situ

Pit near Long Plantation 596752 Section about 4ft

upper head
main head
irregular junction due to heaving of upper growan by frost action
undisturbed growan
floor of pit
recent wash
sound granite

material away to another site (Figure 27, top right). In the last case there is an exact parallel with a child playing with a pile of bricks—removing the top one successively to build a new column, he reverses the order completely. A Dartmoor pit which partly illustrates this feature is the one at Shilstone (659902). Its growan is bedded, clear evidence of transport and deposition by water.

In the pit near Holming Beam, or the Long Plantation (596752) north of Princetown, there is a very irregular contact between the Head and growan (Figure 27, bottom). This is evidence again of the disturbances which occurred during the brief summer seasons, periods when the top foot or two of the ground would thaw out and be severely saturated. The deeper levels of the pits were unaffected and on Dartmoor undisturbed ground is usually seen about six feet below the surface.

South-west of Princetown, about half a mile beyond Devil's

Elbow, is a pit which reveals the effect of drainage on soil development. The uppermost layer is a podsol, a soil type produced where the principal movement of water is downwards. The water carries down all the valuable minerals and rotted plant matter which would be so helpful to the topsoil, leaving it bleached and poor in quality. The washed-out material accumulates in the Brown Earth seen below. Here the concentration of iron minerals hinders the drainage and aggravates the waterlogged conditions in the topsoil still further. With its high rainfall and the absence of long sunny spells to draw water up to the surface and evaporate it, the moor is its own worst enemy for soil improvement.

The Brown Earths of Dartmoor probably developed first under oak forests and the podsols resulted from the continual cutting of these forests and the change towards the present maritime climate with its high rainfall.

While the walker is in this area it is worth while going on to Black Tor. Overlooking the Meavy valley, the tor is an

FIG 28
BLACK TOR   574718 NE

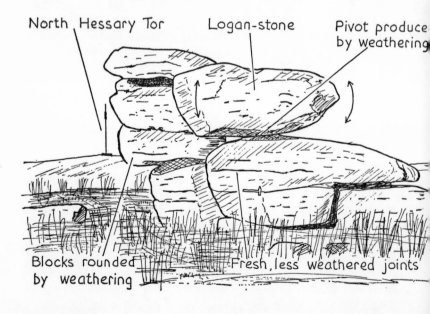

example of a logan stone, a huge block of granite balanced so delicately that it can be rocked by someone standing on its surface (Figure 28). These natural see-saws are the accidental products of joints and weathering. Below, at Black Tor Falls, there are two good blowing houses, legacies of the Dartmoor tin-streamers' activities.

FIG 29

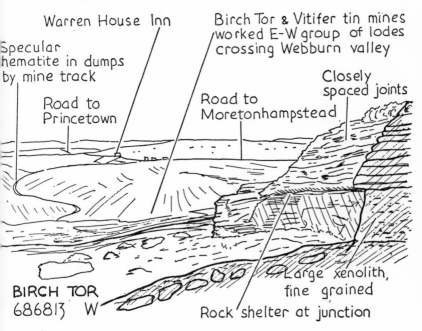

Warren House Inn

Birch Tor & Vitifer tin mines worked E-W group of lodes crossing Webburn valley

Specular hematite in dumps by mine track

Closely spaced joints

Road to Princetown

Road to Moretonhampstead

BIRCH TOR 686813 W

Large xenolith, fine grained

Rock shelter at junction

BIRCH TOR

The Birch Tor area is famous for its mines which lie south of the Warren House Inn, but the tor itself is also worth visiting for it provides an example of a moderately large xenolith. The xenolith can be seen at the south side of the tor (Figure 29), the more coarse-grained granite above it overhanging to form a rock shelter. Carefully searching the face of the tor, the geologist can also discover some fine-grained aplite veins cutting through the older granites.

Mineral collectors will, of course, make straight for the old mine sites below in the West Webburn valley. The dumps and huge gullies dug out here are best reached by the track which runs down from the King's Oven, an ancient smelting site north-east of Warren House Inn. When the track begins to drop more steeply, turn off into the old diggings on the right. Some black tin, plenty of green chlorite and grey specular hematite will soon be found in the reddish-coloured waste.

Most of the excavation and shaft working here was done in the nineteenth century but the mines were worked long before that and probably streamed originally. The gravels in the Webburn valley reach 30ft in depth and the numerous lodes shown on Map 12 would have provided them with a good deal of alluvial tin. However, the valley floor is so saturated that pits cannot be unwatered below 10ft. So the ancient stream-works here must have been confined to the gravels nearest the surface and the lower levels have probably never been touched. Samples taken in them return about 7lb of black tin per ton.

The size of the nineteenth-century surface works and the shallow depths recorded in the shafts confirm that the Birch Tor tin lodes were never very productive—typical of the deeper

MAP 12

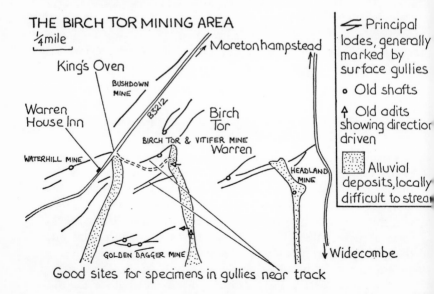

THE BIRCH TOR MINING AREA

¼ mile

Principal lodes, generally marked by surface gullies

o Old shafts

↑ Old adits showing direction driven

Alluvial deposits, locally difficult to stream

King's Oven

BUSHDOWN MINE

Moretonhampstead

B3212

Birch Tor

Warren House Inn

BIRCH TOR & VITIFER MINE

Warren

WATERHILL MINE

HEADLAND MINE

GOLDEN DAGGER MINE

Widecombe

Good sites for specimens in gullies near track

parts of tin zone mineralisation. Tin (cassiterite) can be found in specimens as thin brown veinlets, but it is less common than the quartz and specular hematite which make up the bulk of the vein material. In fact the ore mined here only contained about 2 per cent cassiterite.

The local granite revealed in the dumps is reddish-coloured with large felspars. Aplites can also be found, stained red and often kaolinised where they occur near the vein materials.

The lodes at Birch Tor generally run north-eastwards and, remembering the arrangement of mineral zones around the granite, their presence here on the central moor suggests that the district lies very near the original roof of the granite. If so, there has been very little erosion of the granite mass in this area.

THE CULM OUTLIERS OF SOUTHERN DARTMOOR

Southern Dartmoor is the area south of the Yelverton-Two Bridges-Ashburton road. Its western margin has already been described in connection with the Lee Moor china-clay deposits and the explorer should now make for its southernmost fringe.

Bounded by the A38, this part of Dartmoor receives surprisingly scant attention from tourists speeding westwards to Plymouth. Although it lies within a mile of the main road for some distance, its narrow dead-end lanes have proved impassable for coach tours. With the exception perhaps of Shipley Bridge and the favourite walk up to the Avon Dam, it remains one of the lesser known districts of the moor.

The southern moor is interesting because it has its own drainage system, originating around the ridge crowned by Ryder's Hill (1,690ft) its highest point. Some interesting studies can be made where two of its rivers leave the moor, the Erme and the Avon. Both cross metamorphic rocks and outliers of Carboniferous (Culm) beds. Map 13 shows how both outliers lie between the granite and Devonian beds. In both cases they are entirely within the metamorphic aureole The fact that they were originally shales and calcareous (limestone) beds is known from their reaction to the metamorphism, described below.

The presence of outliers on this part of the moorland boundary confirms how the granite was intruded regardless of the rocks around it, cutting steeply across them and isolating the

MAP 13
(Generalised from maps of the Institute of Geological Sciences with permission of the Director)

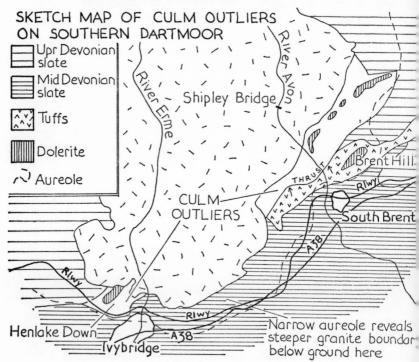

SKETCH MAP OF CULM OUTLIERS ON SOUTHERN DARTMOOR

- Upr Devonian slate
- Mid Devonian slate
- Tuffs
- Dolerite
- Aureole

River Erme

River Avon

Shipley Bridge

CULM OUTLIERS

THRUST

Brent Hill

R.Wy

South Brent

A38

Henlake Down

Ivybridge

A38

R.Wy

Narrow aureole reveals steeper granite boundary below ground here

two outliers from each other. But that is not the whole story. Thrusting and faulting have also helped, separating the outcrops from the next nearest Carboniferous material, three miles to the north at Holne. As Map 13 shows, the larger eastern outlier is bounded on the south by a thrust which continues towards Ashburton and on the east by a tear-fault which is probably part of the Prewley to Dartmouth one of Tertiary age (page 120).

THE METAMORPHIC ROCKS OF SOUTHERN DARTMOOR

The metamorphic effect of Dartmoor was achieved partly by the contact with its heat and partly by the gases and steam which it released. Together they acted on two major groups of sediments along the southern border—a group of fine-grained shale beds and a calcareous group.

The fine-grained shales were completely reconstructed and turned into flinty dark rocks known as hornfels and containing plenty of chiastolite. These can be studied at Pithill, near Ivybridge (see below).

The calcareous group lay further away from the granite and all the normal calcium carbonate of their limestones was replaced by lime-silicates. Lime-silicate rocks have been named 'calcflintas', a very appropriate name as they do fracture rather like flints. They are hard, fine grained and generally grey in colour. Fine banding is an important characteristic of them, and quartz is often found, giving the rock a streaky appearance.

Another feature of the altered calcareous rocks is the formation of common garnets (Almandine) and amphiboles. Garnet is by no means uncommon on Dartmoor. It occurs at Meldon, Burrator and Swell Tor, for example, but before anyone rushes out to find it remember that it is often in reddish-brown veins and seldom of gem quality.

Garnet is a very common product of the metamorphism of clayey limestone beds but it is not confined to the metamorphic zone. It also occurs in the granite where these beds were absorbed into the molten mass on its arrival. Garnets are occasionally found over several square miles of the Erme valley with another characteristic mineral pinite, a variable mixture of white mica and green chlorite. So the Erme valley must have seen a good deal of absorption or lie very near the original roof.

Another mineral to look for is the brown-coloured axinite, developed in the calcareous rocks around Ivybridge and South Brent as a direct result of boron gas emanating from the granite.

IVYBRIDGE

Ivybridge is wedged tightly against the southern slopes of the moor at the exit of the Erme's deep gorge. Following the west bank of the river up Station Road, pass beneath the Viaduct and park at the bend where the rough track to Pithill begins. There is a footpath sign to Henlake Down on the corner.

FIG 30

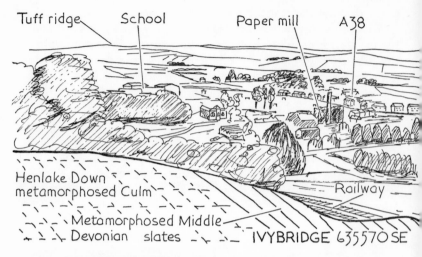

Tuff ridge   School   Paper mill   A38

Henlake Down
metamorphosed Culm   Railway

Metamorphosed Middle
Devonian   slates   IVYBRIDGE 635570 SE

A short distance up the track excavations for a driveway
have exposed the metamorphic rocks and these can be seen
again in a quarry higher up, beyond the second footpath sign
to Henlake Down. This quarry is rather overgrown but its
altered shale beds can be seen best at the northern end. There
is plenty of chiastolite in the slaty beds here.

The bracken and gorse covered slopes of Henlake Down
now come right down to the track, but when woodland begins
again on the upper side a second quarry is reached. While
walking up the track to it, the explorer has, in fact, crossed
the granite boundary and the second quarry reveals a coarsely
crystalline 'blue' granite. It must have assimilated a good
deal of the surrounding beds for it is rich with rectangular
prisms of the mineral cordierite (see Burrator, page 66).

The boundary of the granite can be found in the deep gorge
below, a little north of an old reservoir, or the explorer can
return to the paths onto Henlake Down. The down offers
wonderful views over Ivybridge and the South Hams and there
are small exposures of its metamorphosed dolerites and calcflintas. Henlake Down is part of the 690ft erosion level.

On the way over to South Brent it is worth noting the Rutt
granite quarry, half a mile north of Filham. Felsite in several
colours occurs here in workings which supplied the stone for
the Ivybridge and Cornwood railway viaducts.

SOUTH BRENT

The first spot to make for after passing through the village is Brent Hill and Beara Common. The view of this prominent hill from the A38 at Wrangaton is perhaps one of the best known anywhere along the southern border of the moor. It is best to park near Lutton Farm and walk up the west side.

FIG 31

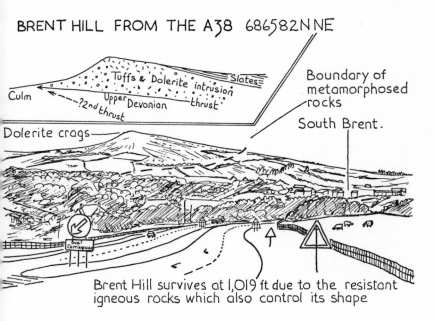

BRENT HILL FROM THE A38 686582 NNE

Boundary of metamorphosed rocks

Culm

Tuffs & Dolerite intrusion — Slates

Upper Devonian — thrust

?2nd thrust

Dolerite crags —

South Brent.

Brent Hill survives at 1,019 ft due to the resistant igneous rocks which also control its shape

The rocks of Brent Hill were intensively deformed before they were metamorphosed and the slopes reveal altered tuffs and ashes, hard dark-grey rocks. Altered green-coloured dolerites outcrop nearer the top of the hill and searching across to the eastern slopes, reddish-coloured garnets and green amphiboles can be found. The latter are glassy, needle-like and sometimes fibrous in appearance. The thrust shown in Map 13 cuts across the northern base of the hill between Bloody Pool and Aish.

Continuing up the Avon Valley, park at Shipley Bridge. A walk up to either Shipley Tor or Black Tor (not to be confused with the Black Tor of the Meavy valley) will yield

FIG 32

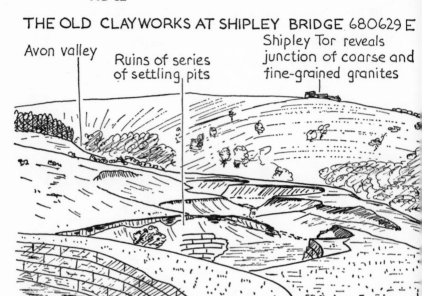

THE OLD CLAYWORKS AT SHIPLEY BRIDGE 680629 E

Avon valley

Ruins of series
of settling pits

Shipley Tor reveals
junction of coarse and
fine-grained granites

coarse and fine-grained granites in contact with each other, best seen near the summit of Shipley Tor.

Shipley Bridge is surrounded by the ruins of ventures in economic geology. Most prominent are the remains of the peat and naphtha works by the car park. On the slopes above, the partly destroyed settling pits of the abandoned South Brent clayworks can be seen. Many of the massive granite slabs have since been taken away for other building purposes. Map 10 shows the sites of these small unsuccessful clayworks on southern Dartmoor. All failed because the felspars in their pits were only partly decomposed.

On the way up to the Avon Dam a stop should be made at the enclosures known as Ryder's Rings, on the west slope of the valley. Here outcrops of fine-grained felsite contain black tourmaline nodules. These have often weathered out and can be found in the topsoil around. Similar nodules can be found up to one and a half inches across, in pink felsite at the Avon Dam. The dam area is also a good site to study the tourmalinisation of the normal granite.

CHAPTER 9

East Dartmoor

Some of the most beautiful scenery found on the borders of Dartmoor occurs on its eastern margin in the Teign and Bovey valleys. The eastern districts attract a great number of tourists from the major resorts of south Devon. Becky Falls, Fingle Gorge, Lustleigh and many other spots are deservedly popular. One tor, however, surpasses all other sites.

HAYTOR ROCKS

A mecca for tourists from the local resorts, the rocks of Haytor are certainly the most famous of Dartmoor tors, and their distinctive twin hump can be seen from a wide area of South Devon. The bracken-covered slopes give way to heather moor near the summit and there are well-trodden grass tracks leading up from Haytor Vale, or the car park to the south.

Haytor is a happy hunting-ground for the geologist; it illustrates so many features of the Dartmoor tors, and offers fine exposures of both 'Tor' and 'Quarry' granites as well as their different reaction to the cold conditions of the Ice Age.

Typically, the actual tor is built of the coarse-grained 'Tor' granite. A large mass of finer-grained granite lies below, and in the western pile its junction is exposed in the north-west face. This lower granite is very fine-grained; quarrymen evidently sampled it but found it too fine to use.

The junction here is also a good example of a rock shelter; another can be found on Bench Tor. These features are the result of Ice Age conditions, when the fine-grained granite body disintegrated more rapidly than the 'Tor' granite above. The Tor granite now overhangs by 2-3ft in places, providing a rough shelter for anyone caught there in a sudden squall.

There are plenty of examples of recent weathering on Haytor. Selecting any vertical joint the student will find a little cone-shaped heap of quartz sand where the joint reaches ground level.

Haytor is sometimes referred to as an 'avenue' tor, one with a broad way through its centre. Once a complete ridge, its

FIG 33

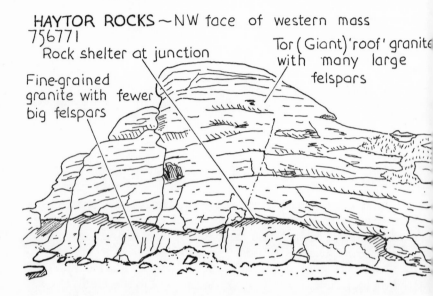

HAYTOR ROCKS ~ NW face of western mass
756771
Rock shelter at junction
Tor (Giant) 'roof' granite with many large felspars
Fine-grained granite with fewer big felspars

central blocks were heaved out to leave two separate humps. Severely cold conditions achieved this, water freezing in the joints expanded, exerting sufficient force to move very large blocks, a feature best appreciated from the air. On west Dartmoor, Great Staple Tor is another example of the avenue type, while Blackingstone Tor, described below, escaped this sort of damage for some reason.

Following the granite down the north-west slopes of Haytor, in about 300yd the geologist reaches the famous quarries, worked intermittently from 1820 to 1919. Here the stone contains fewer large felspars than on the tor. (See page 112.)

Haytor provides the classic relationship of tor and fringing quarries. All who love Dartmoor scenery should be thankful that the lower granite was the one sought for building stone, the tors holding little attraction for the nineteenth-century quarrymen.

MARINERS' COMPASSES

Haytor is prominent because it lies so near the edge of the granite outcrop, the boundary passing between the rock and Haytor Vale. At Haytor Vale an unusual mineral lode was intruded into metamorphosed Culm rocks. Worked in the Haytor and Smallacombe mines it yielded magnetite, a magnetic iron ore also known as lodestone. As long ago as the sixteenth century the Haytor deposits were worked for this magnetite, a splinter of which floating in a bowl of water made an early form of mariner's compass. Specimens are easily identified by their attraction to a magnet and their black colour. White's 1850 *Directory of Devon* records magnetite mining at South Brent as well, 'a piece of it moving a needle at a distance of 9ft'. A wooded cutting by the bend in the road south of the Rock Hotel is about all that can be seen of Haytor mine today. The Smallacombe site is marked by a similar cutting.

MORE EAST DARTMOOR TORS

Heltor Rock is another stupendous vantage point on the eastern fringe of Dartmoor. As Haytor commands the southeast, so Heltor looks over the north-east. Its horizon embraces the great expanse of Culm country with the sandstone trough of Crediton and Bow to the north, and the Exe Valley to the east. Below are the steep slopes of the Teign gorge, their hilltops valuable as Iron Age forts at Prestonbury, Wooston and Cranbrook Castles. To the west, the skyline is broken by the single hump of Blackingstone Rock and farther away there is a distant glimpse of Haytor.

Around Heltor the granite is visible in low, oval outcrops with plenty of large felspar crystals. On top of the rock there are several rock basins, formed by rainwater collecting in hollows on the surface. Rotting occurs and when the water is evaporated away in the sunshine it removes material with it. Repetition gradually deepens the hollows, forming such perfect basins that they look as if they have been carved. In the end, these basins bore right through their slabs, another modern means of tor destruction.

Less than a mile away on the same ridge is Blackingstone

Rock. One of the most unusual on Dartmoor, it looks as if it has been poured out from a jug held just above it. Its joints suggest sticky lumps flowing over each other to make its dome shape. Some of these 'horizontal' joints may have formed following removal of material covering the tor, the loss of weight allowing upward adjustment and release of internal stress caused by the weight of the cover.

FIG 34

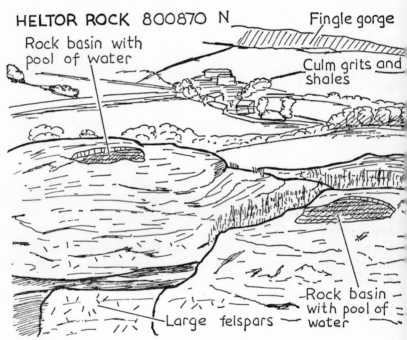

HELTOR ROCK 800870 N

Rock basin with pool of water

Fingle gorge

Culm grits and shales

Large felspars

Rock basin with pool of water

The best access point is a car park just north of the rock. A footpath leads up from the minor road there. From the path the north face appears as a vertical wall of massive proportions, each block rounded by weathering where its joint pattern emerges in the hillside.

Like Haytor, Blackingstone has its quarry, but here the relationship of 'Tor' and 'Quarry' granites is hidden. Blackingstone quarry has swarms of large felspar crystals, arranged in broadly curving rows. It is also a site to find xenoliths (zeen-o-liths), pieces of rocks which fell into the molten granite. Their own chemicals were replaced by those of the granite around them but they can still be spotted by their different grain size. Typical xenoliths here appear as darker fine-grained patches, often rounded in shape as if they had originally been pebbles. Xenoliths can also be found on other parts of Dartmoor—

FIG 35

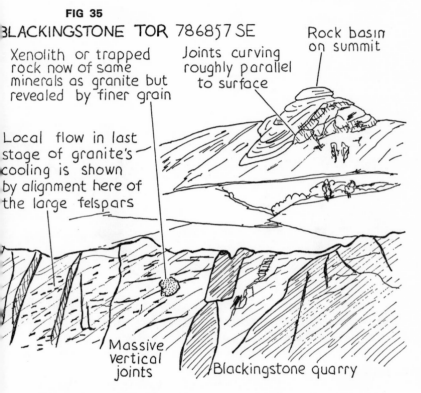

BLACKINGSTONE TOR 786857 SE

Xenolith or trapped rock now of same minerals as granite but revealed by finer grain

Joints curving roughly parallel to surface

Rock basin on summit

Local flow in last stage of granite's cooling is shown by alignment here of the large felspars

Massive vertical joints

Blackingstone quarry

at Honeybag and Chinkwell Tors, near Widecombe, there are rounded pieces of altered dolerite. They were similarly trapped during the arrival of the granite.

POUNDSGATE, LEUSDON AND BUCKLAND

The Webburn valley has some interesting features near Poundsgate and its junction with the Dart. An instructive tour can be made starting from New Bridge.

Going downstream from New Bridge, take the Buckland road for a view of the 690ft erosion surface. The road climbs

G

steeply up the east bank of the Webburn through Great Lot Wood. Figure 36 shows the view westwards over the river. The pattern of woodland and field, of forestry where slopes are steep and cultivation where they are more gentle, emphasises the contrasts between old erosion levels and the deep cuts made in them by the river Dart and its tributaries.

FIG 36

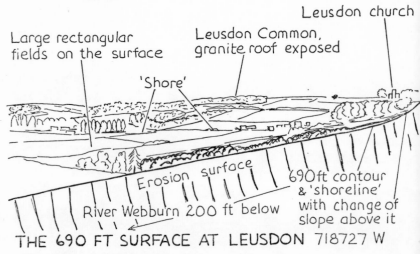

Leusdon church

Large rectangular fields on the surface

Leusdon Common, granite roof exposed

'Shore'

Erosion surface

River Webburn 200 ft below

690ft contour & 'shoreline' with change of slope above it

THE 690 FT SURFACE AT LEUSDON 718727 W

Continuing up the lane the walker reaches Buckland, the village standing on another remnant of the 690ft surface. The deep valley of the Webburn has to be skirted via Cockingford Mill Farm and Ponsworthy to reach the next point of interest on Leusdon Common. Here the roof of the Dartmoor granite is exposed in small outcrops near fields on the south-west side of the common. Fine-grained, pink-coloured granite veins can be traced through rocks spotted with biotite (black mica). Plenty of clitters reveal similar features.

Starting back towards New Bridge, pass through Pounds-gate and make for Leigh Tor. Its rough tumbling outcrop extends right down the hillside almost to the river Dart, surrounded by massive clitters. Leigh Tor is a quartz-schorl dyke (black schorl is another name for tourmaline). It is harder than the Culm rocks around it and forms an upstanding feature, appearing again to the east of the Dart at Holne Chase and Ausewell Rocks.

FIG 37

LEIGH TOR 709715 E

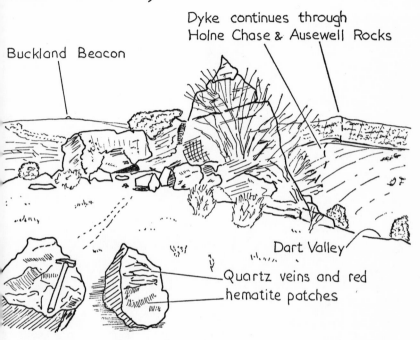

Dyke continues through
Holne Chase & Ausewell Rocks

Buckland Beacon

Dart Valley

Quartz veins and red
hematite patches

Working outwards from the centre of the tor and using solid outcrops rather than clitter, the gradual change from the heart of the dyke to the surrounding rock can be traced. There is a lot of patchy red hematite and the blocks are laced with later veins of white quartz.

THE 1,000 FOOT SURFACE

The river Teign has a special charm, quite different in character from the Dart. The high moorland course of the Teign is shorter and the river spends more time in the border country of Dartmoor where the highest ridges are related to the 1,000ft surface. The level is extensive in the country lying between the river and the A382 through Moretonhampstead. Blackingstone and Heltor, already described, stand on it and

the road from Moretonhampstead to Clifford Bridge crosses
Mardon Down at this height. Well-marked 1,000ft levels also
follow the east side of the Wray brook and the A382 towards
Bovey Tracey.

MAP 14

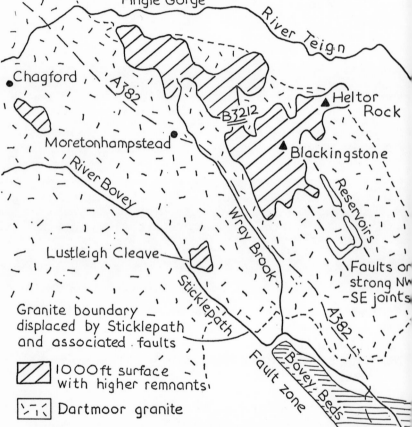

SKETCH MAP OF NW–SE ALIGNMENTS : E DARTMOOR

A good contrast can be made by following the A382 south
along the Wray Valley and then returning to Moretonhampstead along the upland level through Poolmill Cross and
Pepperdon. The explorer might be forgiven for thinking he

had passed through two widely separated districts. The contrast in outlook is amazing, yet the road over the 1,000ft surface lies less than half a mile from its neighbour below.

THE MIDDLE TEIGN VALLEY

Rather a quiet backwater between busier east-west roads, this part of the valley retains a rural charm with its old mills and scattered woodland.

A succession of small mines were active along its slopes in the Christow area, seeking lead and barytes. They all stood on the same N-S lodes, in a belt of country weakened by faulting.

Barytes was produced at Bridford mine half-a-mile west of Bridford Mills. The mineral was obtained from shafts and an opencast quarry which lies within the fork in the lane, its face revealing the tabular appearance and attractive lustre of barytes. It is creamy white, with tinges of brown and yellow in this case and is easily distinguished from calcite (which it strongly resembles) by its weight. Hence the name 'heavy spar' often given to it. Underground, some of the local veins had a banded appearance, earning them the name 'bacon ore'. Crushed to a fine powder, the barytes was used in paint and as a filler in paper, leather goods and other items.

The shaft workings and ruins of the crushing mill lie below the quarry. In the 1920s the ore was sent to Exeter for roasting on steam-heated plates before being picked over by hand and ground to a fine powder. The mine closed in 1956 after a productive life of over a century. Its peak year was 1940 when 21,000 tons were produced.

Near Hennock, and higher up the valley side, is another group of lodes, interesting to modern geologists because they contain the most recently worked mine in Devon. Great Rock mine was in continuous production from 1902 to 1970, producing grey, glittering micaceous haematite. Its apt local name 'shining ore' was adopted by the Geological Survey. The same ore occurs in the Buckfastleigh area and at the mine dumps near Warren House Inn, described in Chapter 8.

There are five lodes at Great Rock, all worked by horizontal tunnels (adits) and some of the entrances can be seen along

FIG 38

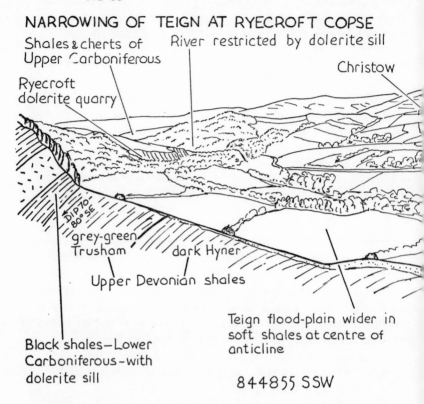

NARROWING OF TEIGN AT RYECROFT COPSE

Shales & cherts of Upper Carboniferous

River restricted by dolerite sill

Christow

Ryecroft dolerite quarry

DIP 70°-80° SE

grey-green Trusham

dark Hyner

Upper Devonian shales

Black shales—Lower Carboniferous—with dolerite sill

Teign flood-plain wider in soft shales at centre of anticline

844855 SSW

the lane round the west side of the hill. Naturally soft, the ore was powdered and then separated from its water in much the same way as tin, on vibrating tables.

Years ago it used to be marketed as pounce, a fine dusting powder used for blotting writing. Powdered cuttlefish shells were generally used for this purpose, but as 'Devonshire sand' the ore was sold extensively in London at 3-8 guineas a ton.

Its scaly nature was lately valued in iron-oxide paints. The scales overlap each other on painted surfaces, giving good protection from rust. The Tamar Bridge was given a coating of this paint because of its exposed position in a salty atmosphere. Battleship-grey paints contained it and the rather dull green of the old Great Western Railway was also due to it. The railway rightly valued its preservative qualities more than a brilliant sheen.

The one-inch OS map sheet 339 reveals a large number of dolerite intrusions in the Middle Teign Valley. Their curving outcrops show how they have been caught up in the local folding, running away from the granite outcrop in the upfolds, curving in towards it where there are downfolds.

Dolerite makes good road metal and ballast. Many quarries have worked the local outcrops but the only one active now is in the dolerite sill by Crockham Bridge. Quarries apart, the dolerites have another important effect on the valley. Figure 38, a view from Great Leigh Farm, shows the wooded ridge crossing the Teign at Ryecroft Copse, east of Christow. Formed of hard dolerites, the feature causes a noticeable narrowing of the Teign as it passes down to Ashton Mill.

Starting about 200 yards north of Ryecroft quarry and the dolerite sill, walk down to Spara Bridge. Several small steep folds can be seen by the road but there seems to be very little variation in the succession. The beds are mostly dark green or black and the survey map shows them as Carboniferous beds. However, revision in 1966-9 proved a range from Upper Devonian to Upper Carboniferous here, a salutary lesson to the amateur geologist in showing just how much information can be obtained from apparently uniform beds.

CHAGFORD AND FINGLE GORGE

Once an important tin-mining centre, the parish of Chagford is strewn with the tell-tale hummocks of old stream works. The town lies in a broad bowl of granite country, close to the Sticklepath Fault (Chapter 11) and drained by the river Teign.

The Teign pays scant attention to the fault, only a small stream rising near Meldon Hall follows the Sticklepath break down the west side of Chagford. From Nattadon Common the walker can trace the Teign eastwards across the open landscape to Hunters Tor where, virtually passing through a wall, the river suddenly leaves the granite country and enters the majestic gash of Fingle Gorge, cutting deeply through high ground formed of Culm beds.

It all seems topsy-turvy. Granite normally forms the higher resistant ground so why is it obviously weaker than the Culm here? Was the broad bowl around Chagford once a lake like the Bovey Basin, a lake which was only drained when the Fingle Gorge had been deepened enough to make an outlet? Why should the Teign choose to go to Fingle at all rather than follow the easy, faulted courses of the river Bovey or the Wray Brook?

Time and the order of events provide the answer. The Teign, one of the early eastward-flowing rivers, was already in the grip of Fingle Gorge long before the Sticklepath tear-fault and neighbouring faults occurred. Their influence was not sufficient to make it turn aside from its task; in fact, they helped it in other ways for as the river lowered its bed in the gorge it was able to open up the broad granite bowl above. The granite there was already weak through rotting. The exceptionally large number of tourmaline veins in the district had seen to that and the faults added to its destruction.

The broad bowl in which Chagford lies is due, then, to the weaker local granite and the river Teign. No lake ever existed here—a lake could only have survived if its bed was deeper than the outlet through Fingle Gorge and then it would have left lake-clays and other deposits over the Chagford area. There is no trace of any such feature in the district.

CHAPTER 10

Quarries, Moorstone and Building

The stonemason's craft is a fascinating one. Before the invention of bricks and concrete, his skill was in universal demand for all types of buildings. Nowadays his art is only seen on more special occasions—an important building, a major bridge or something similar, and generally it is straightforward blocks or slabs for wall linings. There is little carving done.

So for much of the time we must content ourselves with admiring the work of his ancestors in older buildings. There was certainly no shortage of building stones in Devon. The use of the Exeter volcanic stones is obvious all over that district, the centre of old Paignton was built of the local New Red Sandstones, and limestone was dominant in older parts of Torquay and Plymouth.

No one has really plotted on maps the areas over which our Devon building stones were used, and it is safe to assume in advance that the better quality stones will have spread further afield than the poorer. The cream Beer Stone has a national fame and also graces many Devon church screens, whereas the rather coarse New Red Sandstone is seldom found much beyond its own outcrops.

Within the country itself there is one stone which has spread more widely than any other—the Dartmoor granite. In one form or another it has penetrated the territory of every other Devon building stone and yet, because of its abundance on the surface of the moor, it has hardly ever taken second place to another stone in its own territory.

Good building stone must have strength and durability. Years ago temporary buildings were unknown and designers wanted to be sure that what they erected would stand the test of time. The best stones are generally those with a medium grain because they can be evenly dressed. They also weather well, being less susceptible to frost or chemical action, and retain an even surface. Now Dartmoor granite obtained from areas where its grain is good and even, has a crushing strength well beyond the average demands likely to be made on it, but may at first seem to fall short on other requirements, particularly when we remember the part weathering played in attacking the moorland surface and also the weakness of its joint systems.

However, the reader will soon recall that the joints disappear with depth, so uniform blocks will be available from workings far enough below the surface. Secondly, weathering cannot be so effective on such blocks as it is on the well-jointed moorland surface. The fresh granite is even-grained and close textured, its crystals closely knit together so that very little water can penetrate it to rot it chemically or split it mechanically before it has formed a seasoned crust.

Dartmoor granite has been valued over the centuries for its strength and durability. Yet, surprisingly, its use was restricted to the surface slabs or 'moorstone' and quarries were not opened until the nineteenth century.

MOORSTONE

The ample clitters served all man's needs from the Bronze Age, and they were still preferred by some in the nineteenth century after the quarries had begun. The use prehistoric man made of moorstone for his field boundaries and homes is obvious in the hut circles and enclosures which abound all over the moor.

At later dates colonisation encouraged its use, the clearance of land for farming supplying all the stone needed for house and hedges. The early farmhouses were built on the rubble-filled system. A wall of considerable thickness was commenced, its inner and outer faces being of dry-walled undressed stones, while the space between was filled at random with smaller material. In plan they were long-houses (Figure 39), a central passage across the building giving access to the animals' quarters on one side and the home on the other.

In the fourteenth century, builders began to dress the moorstone rather than use it just as they found it, at first in the more heavy items like quoins and buttresses but later in more

FIG 39

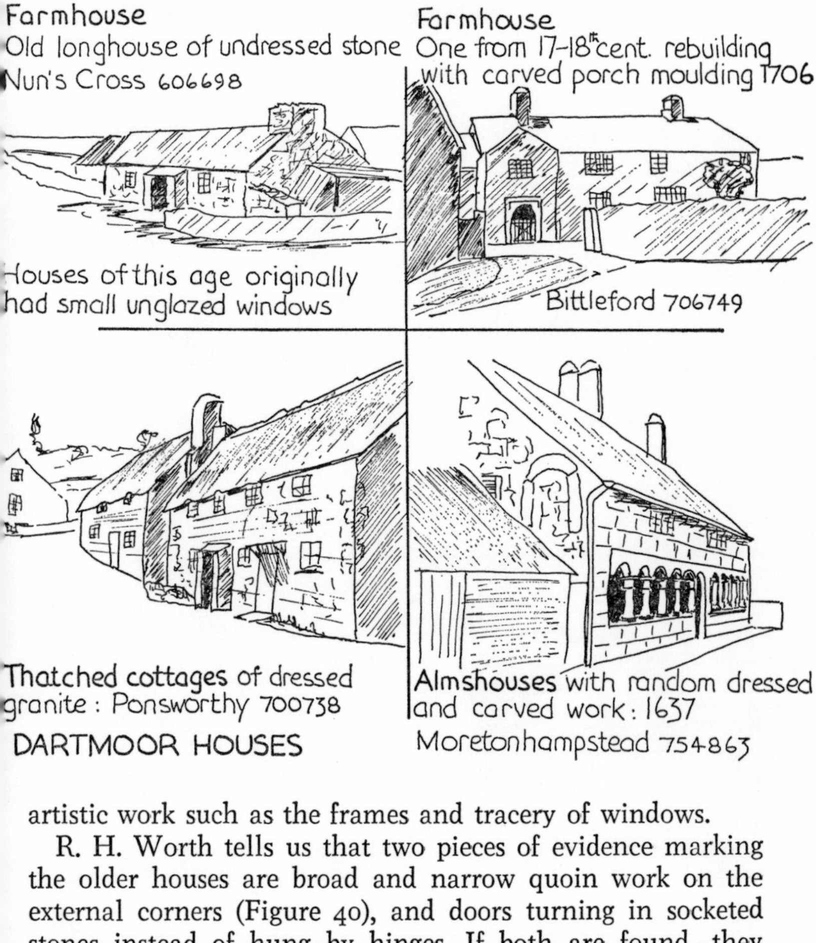

Farmhouse
Old longhouse of undressed stone
Nun's Cross 606698

Farmhouse
One from 17-18th cent. rebuilding
with carved porch moulding 1706

Houses of this age originally
had small unglazed windows

Bittleford 706749

Thatched cottages of dressed
granite : Ponsworthy 700738
DARTMOOR HOUSES

Almshouses with random dressed
and carved work : 1637
Moretonhampstead 754863

artistic work such as the frames and tracery of windows.

R. H. Worth tells us that two pieces of evidence marking the older houses are broad and narrow quoin work on the external corners (Figure 40), and doors turning in socketed stones instead of hung by hinges. If both are found, they date the building as prior to 1600. Broad and narrow quoin work can be seen still and there are more recent but thinner slabbed versions of it about; for example, the gunpowder works built around the Cherry Brook, near Postbridge, in the nineteenth century. Here the explorer can easily see massive walls, broad and narrow quoins and rubble fill.

One fascinating feature of Devonshire housing is the use of granite beyond the moorland border. This was particularly common where rivers leave the moor, acting as natural free transport for the material. The Erme is a good example. Ivy-bridge, tucked closely at the foot of the moor, has a lot of granite housing as would be expected, but it is also found down the valley in field and cottage walls at Ermington. Examina-

FIG 40

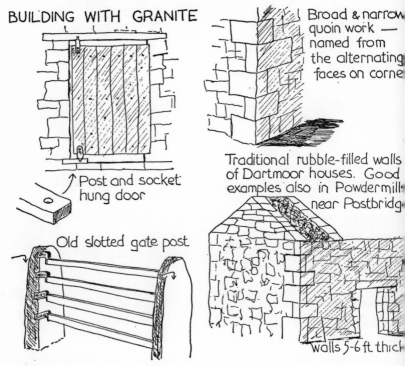

BUILDING WITH GRANITE

Broad & narrow quoin work — named from the alternating faces on corner

Post and socket hung door

Old slotted gate post

Traditional rubble-filled walls of Dartmoor houses. Good examples also in Powdermill near Postbridge

walls 5-6 ft thick

tion of these walls clearly shows the blocks as waterworn, having been obtained from the river bed and used direct in field walls and only roughly dressed on interior faces for cottage construction.

Many Dartmoor farmhouses and manor houses were entirely rebuilt after the time of Elizabeth I and the work was all done in dressed stone. Many people preferred dressed moorstone to quarried stone up to the nineteenth century, too—probably because they felt it was well seasoned, having lost any weaker crust already, and also because the cores were bound to be stout, resistant material .The sett-making industry of Staple Tors in the 1870s is an example of the continued use of moorstone.

Moorstone found many other uses apart from building, particularly for the larger, more durable household articles : water and feeding troughs, gateposts, querns, cider and cheese presses, for example.

In addition to hand querns for grinding grain at home, it was also widely used for millstones. Two lying in the sands at Lannacombe, near Start Point, prove that those granite stones were employed right down to the shores of the county. As millstones the granite could not compete with the composite French stones, or burr stones, from Rouen, but it could do well in the South West against the Pennine Millstone Grit products, or Derbyshire Peak stones as they were known. Used for the coarser grains, the granite stones usually ended their milling days far thinner than they had started and, like most solid, single-piece stones, can now be found doing duty as doorsteps or paving the yard of many an old watermill.

The quarries also produced domestic items and at many spots on the moor completed or broken samples can be seen, sometimes pieces which fell off the local tramway during removal. But it is odd to realise that it was mainly the clitters of destroyed Tor granite which supplied our needs up to the nineteenth century. For further details of housing and moorstone articles see R. H. Worth's *Dartmoor*—the 'Dartmoor House' and the 'Moorstone Age'—and the various papers of N. W. Alcock in recent volumes of *Transactions of Devonshire Association*.

WORKING THE GRANITE

Stonemasons are experts at locating the weakness in rocks, caused perhaps by cleavages or flaws in the minerals present. The old masons had to be, to split the stones by the old methods of grooving and wedging or by the feather and tares. Anyone who has tried either method will know how much the grain of the rock matters.

The familiar joints of the moorland surface areas were an obvious means of removing blocks in all but the deepest quarries, but it still needed a good knowledge of the stone to square up smaller pieces from these before dressing could begin.

Figure 41 illustrates the two older methods. The feathers

FIG 41

SPLITTING GRANITE SLABS

Wedge & groove : groove cut first by chisel

Using the jumper

One or two men hammering

Jumper held and rotated by another

Feathers and tare were used in short cylindrical holes bored with the jumper

tare

feathers

Wedge splitting left squarish notched edges

Cylindrical notches where jumper was used

and tare method came into use in the early nineteenth century when quarrymen introduced the drill or jumper, long used in mining. Hence the round notches on worked stones. They are the remains of the little cylinders which were bored first to take the feathers and tare, so stones which bear them must have been cut sometime since 1800.

One can often find unsuccessful attempts, too, the result perhaps of a half-hearted try at splitting a stone that was partly blocking a farm track. There are several such examples around Burrator, some with a tare still jammed in one of the sockets.

In complete contrast, modern working at Merrivale (described below) is done by cutting the granite with gas torches.

DARTMOOR GRANITE QUARRIES

Over the centuries there can hardly be a spot on Dartmoor that has not seen granite working in some form. The nineteenth-century quarries localised its use, however, and increased the output considerably. Unfortunately, detailed records are scanty and quarrying must be one of the worst documented industries in history. Even today little information can be gathered about working quarries, particularly those belonging to large companies who keep wary eyes on their competitors.

MAP 15

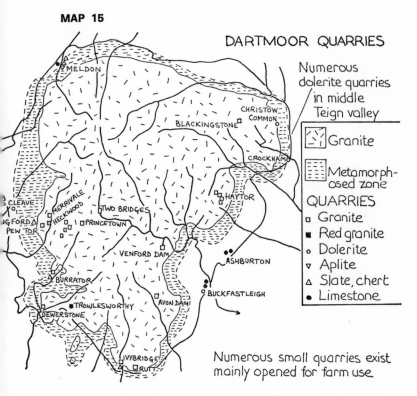

DARTMOOR QUARRIES

Numerous dolerite quarries in middle Teign valley

- ░ Granite
- ▦ Metamorphosed zone

QUARRIES
- □ Granite
- ■ Red granite
- ○ Dolerite
- ▽ Aplite
- △ Slate, chert
- ● Limestone

Numerous small quarries exist mainly opened for farm use

Some Dartmoor works are well-documented, though seldom so from a geologist's viewpoint of the quality and value put upon the stone, while others can only be dated approximately. Haytor and the Walkhampton Common group started around 1820, Pew Tor worked in the 1850s, Merrivale from 1876 and so on—all in the period 1820-80 and in most cases they were disused before the end of the century, the continued working at Merrivale being the most notable exception. We must not, however, forget the sporadic working at Blackingstone (Figures 35 and 43).

The quarries can be divided into two types : large commercial ventures selling to a variety of outlets, like Haytor and those on Walkhampton Common and, secondly, smaller-scale works which were opened for particular purposes. The latter can be dated precisely; for example, Burrator built from stone taken just inside the dam in 1893-8 and heightened using the quarries on the Dousland Road in 1928, page 65. Or again, the use of Heckwood Tor granite for the Plymouth Breakwater, constructed 1817-41, of Rutt quarry for the railway viaducts at Cornwood and Ivybridge, and Venford quarry which was opened to build the dam for Paignton's reservoir. Map 15 shows the more important sites worked on the moor.

HAYTOR QUARRIES

The Haytor quarries were among the largest worked in that century and the nature of their stone can still be studied in most of them, although one is now a reservoir. The most celebrated use was in the reconstruction of London Bridge in

FIG 42

HAYTOR QUARRIES AT WORK about 1825

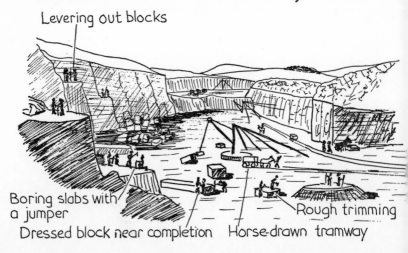

Levering out blocks

Boring slabs with a jumper

Dressed block near completion

Rough trimming

Horse-drawn tramway

FIG 43

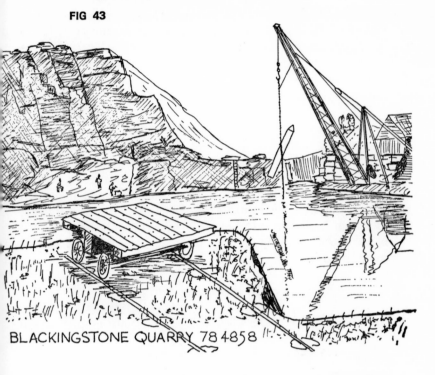

BLACKINGSTONE QUARRY 78 4858

1825. As an interesting footnote, those stones returned to Dartmoor's Merrivale quarry for individual packing before being exported to the United States for the re-erection of the bridge at Lake Havasu City, Arizona (1970).

The celebrated stone-railed tramway was the most peculiar use of the Haytor granite and its higher section near the quarries is now an ancient monument. The prosperity which built it was short-lived, however, and due to lack of trade the tramway had become disused by 1858. The quarries went on in a small way into the 1880s and their size is testimony to the intensive working which took place in the earlier prosperity. These quarries worked the blue or main type of granite, stone which was less coarsely crystalline than the Tor granite on Haytor Rocks above.

Perhaps the most interesting quarry now is the small one just north-west of Haytor and a little above the main quarries served by the tramway. It lies directly over the tor, on the opposite slope to the roadside car park, but it is not visible

H

from the Rocks—you have to start walking down the slopes to find it. The quarry has a fine aplite dyke running parallel to its inner face and the contact with the normal granite of the rest of the working is easily traced. The normal granite here is the Tor variety, but with fewer large felspars than on the Rocks above.

BLACKINGSTONE QUARRY

This is another quarry worth visiting on the eastern part of the moor. It contains small xenoliths and its felspars show some late flow movements in the stone, page 96. Figure 43 shows the massive jointing of the granite at this quarry, although its periodical working is now by explosives for road metal rather than by prising out these huge slabs for monumental work.

MERRIVALE QUARRY

Opened in 1876, the Merrivale quarry once employed 170

FIG 44

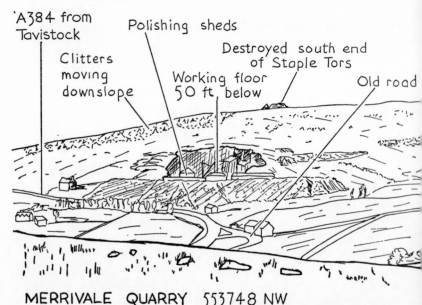

A384 from Tavistock
Polishing sheds
Clitters moving downslope
Destroyed south end of Staple Tors
Working floor 50 ft below
Old road

MERRIVALE QUARRY 553748 NW

men and created the hamlet which lies below. Seen from the road, it has some towering man-made clitter. Crossing, in his *Dartmoor Worker*, describes the great variety of items made at the beginning of the century; channelling, kerbing, pillars. Before tarmac roads, setts were important; most Plymouth streets were paved with them and plenty can still be seen there. The stone, cut now with gas torches, is mainly used in polished facing slabs. Devon County Hall, New Scotland Yard, improvements to the Thames Embankment and Black-friars Bridge are examples. Merrivale granite is also in use in the new London Bridge.

The quarry polishes granites from many other parts of the world, and the black Canadian, or the beautiful deep-velvet Larvikite with its sky blue flakes, provide startling contrasts to the local grey colour. After a visit the observer will soon spot them in the shop fronts of many high-street stores. Permission to visit the works must be obtained beforehand, of course.

WALKHAMPTON COMMON QUARRIES

The quarries worked here include King Tor, Foggintor and Swell Tor, and a smaller excavation to the s-sw at Ingra Tor. Stone for the building of Princetown was obtainable from this part of the moor in the eighteenth century, but it was the building of the Plymouth & Dartmoor tramway up to Prince-town in 1823 which started the great commercial development.

The best way to reach the quarries is to walk along the track from the Tavistock-Princetown road, which begins at the old chapel and runs south past Yellowmeade Farm (Map 16).

The granite in the area is light grey in colour with large white felspars and a good deal of white mica present. There are gigantic spoil tips—which would hardly be affected by a little hammering!—and the inclined plane used to get stone down from the higher levels at Swell Tor is also interesting. It worked by chains running on rollers.

LESS COMMON DARTMOOR STONES

Mention must also be made of two other stones worked for limited periods on the moor, the Trowlesworthy red granite

MAP 16

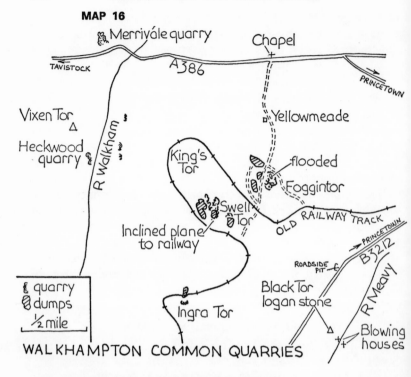

WALKHAMPTON COMMON QUARRIES

and the buff-coloured Roborough Stone.

The Trowlesworthy granite outcrops at the tors of that name, and its special mineral character is described on page 46. The stone was worked up to about 1880 from a small quarry by Little Trowlesworthy Tor and was regarded as a fine granite. It took a good polish.

The Roborough Stone, quarried on Roborough Down, is a fine-grained elvan material (quartz porphyry). It differs from granite in having hardly any sparkling mica in it. The stone was obtained from dykes which cut east-west across the down, forming ridges like the one which crosses the road north of the AA box. The workings are shallow and little remains to be seen, but there are plenty of examples of its use in local churches, Tamerton Foliot and Plympton St Mary for example, as it was a favourite stone for carved items.

The Meldon quarries are described in Chapter 11 since, although they are fascinating geologically, their products have not been used for building purposes.

Northern Dartmoor

A striking feature of both northern and eastern Dartmoor is the NW-SE trend of much of the countryside. The one-inch tourist map of Dartmoor shows it very well, in the Bovey valley, the Wray Brook, Kennick and Tottiford reservoir valleys. Their pattern is, inevitably, emphasised by the local road network.

All these valleys probably follow NW-SE faults, the largest and most important being the one responsible for the direction of the river Bovey. It is known as the Sticklepath Fault.

THE STICKLEPATH FAULT

One evening in 1955 Sticklepath, near Okehampton, was shaken by an earth tremor. The village stands directly on the fault, a great crack which runs right across Devon, and the most famous of a series of NW-SE tear faults in south-west England which date from Tertiary times.

Faults are lines of weakness and fracture, rarely formed in a single movement. Minor adjustments can spread over millions of years, as the 1955 tremor at Sticklepath shows. Stresses build up gradually in the rocks and their typically sudden release causes the earth tremor. Most faults produce vertical movements but tear-faults are the less common horizontal type where one piece of countryside slides by another.

Scissors and paper can easily reproduce this sort of thing. Cut out an outline of Devon and mark on it the positions of Sticklepath and the river Bovey. Draw a line through them, right across the piece of paper. Now cut the outline in two along it and you have a Sticklepath Fault. Place the two pieces of paper side by side on a flat surface and slip them to and fro along the junction. You are making the movement of a tear-fault.

The Sticklepath Fault probably begins off Tor Bay, near Berry Head, and passes up through the Torre valley and Aller Vale towards Newton Abbot. In this area its movement probably split the once continuous outcrop of Devonian rocks now found on the opposite sides of the fault at Kingskerswell and Torquay. You can go back to the paper model again and, trac-

MAP 17

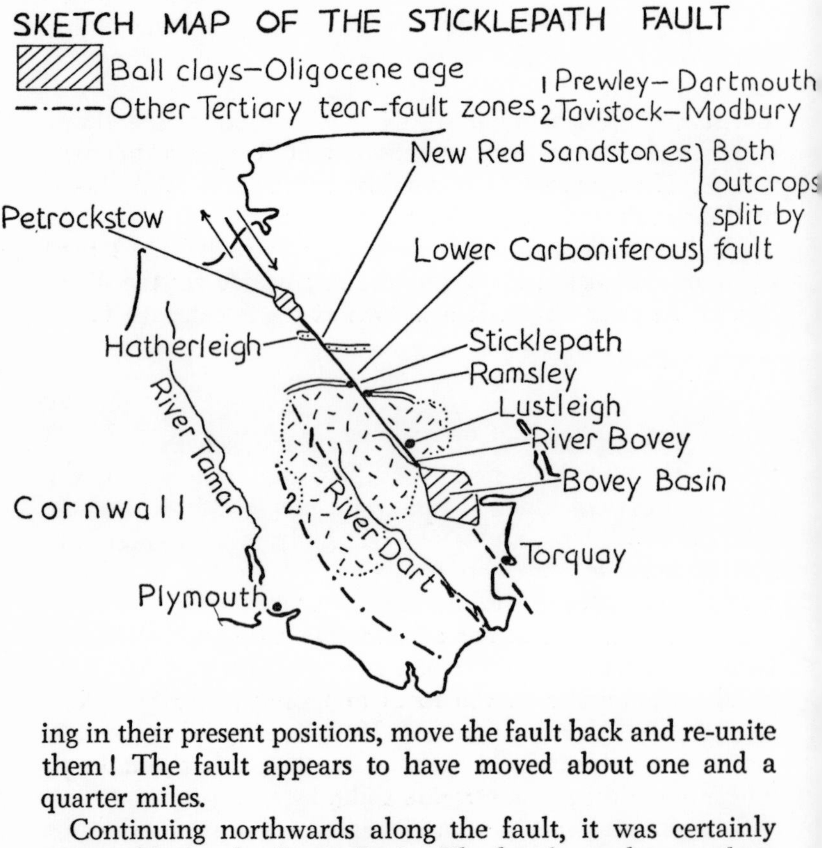

SKETCH MAP OF THE STICKLEPATH FAULT

Ball clays—Oligocene age
—·—·— Other Tertiary tear-fault zones

1 Prewley— Dartmouth
2 Tavistock—Modbury

New Red Sandstones ⎱ Both
                         ⎰ outcrops
                           split by
Lower Carboniferous ⎱ fault

Petrockstow

Hatherleigh

River Tamar

Cornwall

Plymouth

River Dart

Sticklepath
Ramsley
Lustleigh
River Bovey
Bovey Basin

Torquay

ing in their present positions, move the fault back and re-unite them! The fault appears to have moved about one and a quarter miles.

Continuing northwards along the fault, it was certainly responsible for the Bovey Basin. The break can be traced up the river Bovey at Lustleigh, crossing the Teign just west of Chagford. The river Teign was apparently unaffected by it, as described on page 103.

As the fault approaches Sticklepath itself there is more evidence of the displacement along it. The site of the Green-hill mine above the village stands within view of the dumps of Ramsley mine to the south. Both worked copper and arsenic lodes in the belt of Lower Carboniferous beds which follow the northern fringe of Dartmoor.

FIG 45

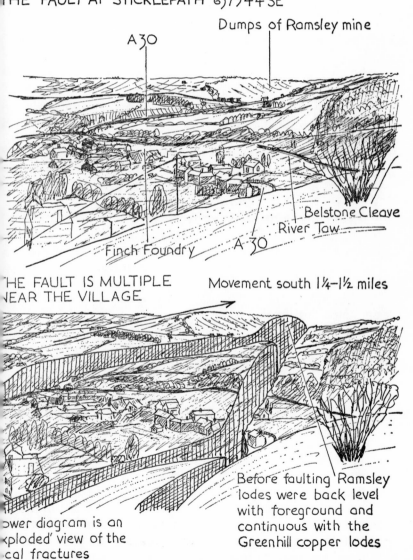

THE FAULT AT STICKLEPATH 637944 SE

Dumps of Ramsley mine

A 30

Belstone Cleave
River Taw

Finch Foundry   A 30

THE FAULT IS MULTIPLE NEAR THE VILLAGE

Movement south 1¼–1½ miles

Before faulting Ramsley lodes were back level with foreground and continuous with the Greenhill copper lodes

Lower diagram is an 'exploded' view of the local fractures

Now 1¼ miles apart, the two mines are, in fact, on the same lode but their sites were separated and moved apart by the faults. Their abandoned workings are some of the best visual evidence found anywhere along the fault today (Figure 45).

North-westwards its continuation breaks up the western end of the New Red Sandstone outcrop of Jacobstowe and Hatherleigh and passes through the ball-clay producing area of Petrockstow. These clays are similar to those of the Bovey Basin. The Sticklepath Fault finally reaches the North Devon coast west of Bideford.

Another tear fault can be seen on northern Dartmoor at Prewley, and runs across to Dartmouth eventually (page 88). The West Okement river follows it for two miles below Black Tor to Vellake Corner, and to the north-west beyond Sourton Down similar alignments can be noticed in the streams flowing towards Ashbury and North Lew.

The other mid-Tertiary faults run from Tavistock to Modbury (see Map 2) and from Cambeak in Cornwall to Plymouth. There are two more farther west in Cornwall.

Apart from visual evidence such as Ramsley mine, the explorer should always examine the map around any known fault-zone. Faults are obvious lines of weakness for rivers to attack and they may give one river an advantage over another, leading to river capture.

The small rivers south of the Taw, the Ramsley Stream and the Blackaton Brook, certainly have some marked right-angle bends in them where they meet the Sticklepath Fault and turn to flow along its route. The Geological Survey memoir for Okehampton (1969) suggests that this is the case. The Blackaton Brook may have captured parts of the Ramsley Stream and led them away towards the Teign.

MELDON

There are four rock groups involved in the succession around northern Dartmoor but the pattern they make on the map is a very complex one. Folding, faulting and dyke formation have created such rapid variations and repetition of beds that at Meldon a dozen changes in rock type can be counted in just over a mile as the explorer approaches the granite margin.

The geological succession around northern Dartmoor is :-

Upper Carboniferous	Crackington Formation	Sandstones, many hundreds of feet thick
Lower Carboniferous	Meldon Chert Formation	250ft thick
	Meldon Slates, Quartzites and Volcanic Group	400-500ft thick
	Meldon Slates with Lenticles	over 400ft thick

The Carboniferous-Devonian boundary lies within the lowest group, the Slates with lenticles.

FIG 46

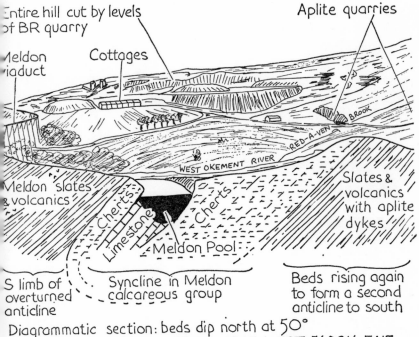

Entire hill cut by levels of BR quarry

Aplite quarries

Meldon Viaduct

Cottages

Meldon slates & volcanics

WEST OKEMENT RIVER

RED-A-VEN BROOK

Slates & volcanics with aplite dykes

Cherts

Limestone

Cherts

Meldon Pool

S limb of overturned anticline

Syncline in Meldon calcareous group

Beds rising again to form a second anticline to south

Diagrammatic section: beds dip north at 50°

MELDON QUARRIES FROM THE WEST 560916 ENE

The best way to reach Meldon is to turn off the A30 opposite Betty Cottle's Cottage and follow the road up to the railway viaduct (Figure 46). The West Okement river, young and scenically beautiful, gives little hint of the structures around it and it is in the quarries that dolerite intrusions and aplite dykes can be seen among the folds. Starting at the bottom of the sequence, the Slates with lenticles were originally sea-bed muds, although they do not contain any fossils. They are distinguished by their small-scale, tight folding and by the lenticles which are concentrations of carbonates and silicates. They can be studied in crags on the west bank of the Okement below Meldon viaduct (564925).

The second group in the sequence is perhaps the least interesting for the Meldon Slates have been so heavily metamorphosed that it is difficult to tell their original nature. Among them are the volcanic beds, tuffs formed by explosive volcanoes. A small disused quarry in this group can be seen at the western end of Sticklepath between the track up to the old Greenhill mine and Skaigh Lane.

FIG 47

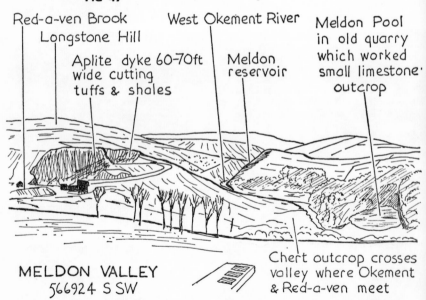

Red-a-ven Brook
Longstone Hill
Aplite dyke 60-70ft wide cutting tuffs & shales

West Okement River
Meldon reservoir

Meldon Pool in old quarry which worked small limestone outcrop

MELDON VALLEY
566924 S SW

Chert outcrop crosses valley where Okement & Red-a-ven meet

The Meldon Cherts mark the top of the Lower Carboniferous beds and they include cherts, limestones and black muds. The latter are now black shales, of course. The first quarry to visit is Meldon Pool. If you have not already crossed the river to see the Slates with lenticles, do so at the footbridge beneath the railway viaduct and continue up the west bank to the flooded working. Now used for water supply, its 130ft depth is testimony to the value of this narrow limestone outcrop within the chert beds. It supported limekilns, as did other small outcrops at Bridestowe, South Tawton and Drewsteignton, described later.

Posidonia becheri is a notable fossil in the black shales and can be found in scattered, flattened shells, sometimes one valve sometimes both. The most likely place to find them is about 100yd below the higher footbridge. Leaving Meldon Pool, cross to the east bank of the river again and turn downstream as if returning to the railway viaduct. The fossil occurs in the river bank in a black shale outcrop.

Straddling the Red-a-ven Brook opposite are the Meldon Aplite quarries. Written permission must be obtained before entering these or the British Rail quarry described below. Some features can be seen from outside; alternatively, the walker can explore the Red-a-ven as far as the mine dumps and the granite boundary, but of course this is no substitute for a visit to the quarries since so many interesting minerals occur in them.

The Meldon Aplite has a chemical composition which makes it unique in Britain. The largest dyke occurs on the southern side of the Red-a-ven Brook, an intrusion 60-70ft thick can be traced diagonally up the two working levels. The higher margins of the dyke are marked by rotted brown shales, and in the eastern part of the top level specimens of axinite, a dark brown mineral, are obtainable. More minerals can be collected from the working on the north side of the brook where the aplite occurs in four smaller dykes. In the joint planes green tourmaline and blue-green apatite occur, while attractive violet-coloured veins of fluorite are common.

In the railway quarry the north-east face is the most rewarding and best exposed at present (Figure 48). The northerly end of this face is in the calcareous beds of the Meldon Cherts, so metamorphism has produced some attractive minerals here. Garnet occurs in brown veins at the lower end, and in the central area there is wollastonite, whose white, silky-lustred rosettes are easily spotted. The face also reveals how the folds at Meldon, leaning towards the granite boundary, are broken by faults and thrust planes.

FIG 48

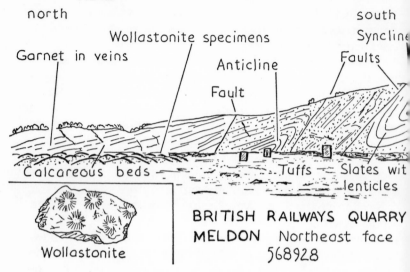

THE LIMESTONES AROUND NORTHERN DARTMOOR

The general improvement in agriculture in the eighteenth and nineteenth centuries led at first to a great increase in the use of manures which could be obtained locally. Seaweed, sea-sand with a high shell content, and burned limestone were in great demand and were carried onto the fields with what later proved to have been an excessive zeal in some cases.

The districts around northern Dartmoor had little chance of obtaining sea-sand or seaweed manures because of their distance from the coast or navigable rivers. They were isolated from the trade in South Wales limestone which was sold along the North Devon coast, and also from the major producing districts, such as Tor Bay and Plymouth, in South Devon. As a result the very limited outcrops of limestone occurring in the Lower Carboniferous beds near the border of the moor assumed an importance almost as great as if they had been gold mines.

Map 18 shows the distribution of the outcrops and the limekilns they served. The walker will have already discovered two of these kilns at Meldon Pool. When Charles Vancouver wrote his *General View of the Agriculture of Devon* in 1808 he reported that the Meldon kilns were then out of use, but that lime was then available locally, at 1s 4d the double Winchester bushel, from Sourton, Bridestowe, Lewtrenchard and Lifton.

In terms of area, the South Tawton quarries must certainly be the largest workings, and South Tawton itself one of Devon's least spoilt villages. The deserted quarries lie just to the north. Heavily overgrown, they once yielded the dark grey Lower Carboniferous limestones. The quarries covered almost the entire outcrop here and in the northernmost face the limestones can be seen dipping northwards at an angle of about 18 degrees. Ruins of massive limekilns stand in the workings, once served by water-powered ramps which took the stone straight from quarry floor to charging platform (Figure 49).

MAP 18

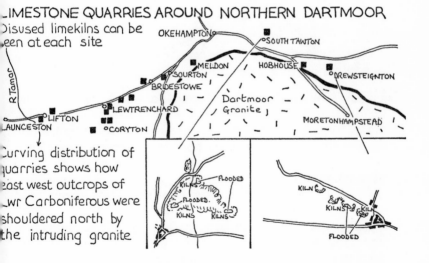

LIMESTONE QUARRIES AROUND NORTHERN DARTMOOR

Disused limekilns can be seen at each site

Curving distribution of quarries shows how east west outcrops of Lwr Carboniferous were shouldered north by the intruding granite

The Drewsteignton quarries were also large. There the workings were reported as 224ft and the main limestone bed is certainly 150ft thick. Like South Tawton, Sourton and Stone Farm quarry at Bridestowe, the Drewsteignton works are flooded now. This is evidence of the depth of working at all these sites around northern Dartmoor. The limestone outcrops within the Meldon Cherts are so restricted in area that

FIG 49

Section in calcareous shales and
limestones dipping north 18°

Kiln wells
loaded at top

Posidonias
found at base

Deep flooded
working

Ramp to kilns

Water powered winch

Calcined lime withdrawn through fire-grate

SOUTH TAWTON QUARRY Northern area 658950NE

the quarries had to go deep to remain in production. Deeper
works meant more expense in pumping water out and lifting
out the stone. The Drewsteignton dumps have been used for
road fill recently.

Another site which illustrates the value put on these limestones and the difficult working that winning them involved
is the quarry at Lewtrenchard. At Lew Quarry (464862) the
limestone beds dip beneath such a great thickness of slate and
chert that, unable to face the increasing waste problem from
above, they drove galleries into the quarry face for as far as
they dared go without bringing the beds above down on their
heads.

OKEHAMPTON

Reference to the Okehampton one-inch geological map

(Sheet 324) shows how all the complex Lower Carboniferous outcrops of northern Dartmoor—Meldon, the limestone pockets described above, etc—are part of a much-faulted and folded anticline which comes up through the Upper Carboniferous beds and is therefore properly called an inlier.

The Upper Carboniferous beds outcrop between it and the granite to the south, and on the north extend away as a great mass of shales and sandstones to form mid-Devon. Okehampton, the capital of northern Dartmoor, stands on these endless and rather monotonous beds and even geologists have to admit that, inland at any rate, they are rather dull and uninteresting.

Around Okehampton, though, there are several sites where

FIG 50

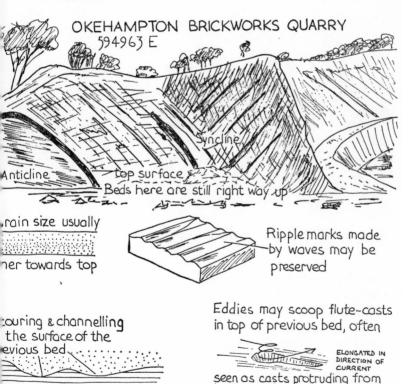

OKEHAMPTON BRICKWORKS QUARRY
594963 E

Syncline

Anticline   top surface
Beds here are still right way up

rain size usually
ner towards top

Ripple marks made by waves may be preserved

:ouring & channelling the surface of the evious bed

Eddies may scoop flute-casts in top of previous bed, often

ELONGATED IN DIRECTION OF CURRENT

seen as casts protruding from bottom of new bed above

OME OF THE SEDIMENTARY STRUCTURES WHICH CAN BE SED TO TELL THE ORIGINAL ATTITUDE OF THE BEDS

fold features can be studied in them. About a mile north of the town on the Exbourne road stands the old Okehampton Brickworks. The beds worked there were the shales and sandstones of the Crackington Formation, the lower part of the Upper Carboniferous material. The beds used to be picked out by hand in the old days as only the shale was required, but inevitably some sandstones got in and the bricks were always rather gritty in texture.

FIG 51

586948 W

Nose of overturned anticline in sandstones of Crackington Formati

Top of bed originally

Normal and overturned folds reversing top & bottom of beds

TOP
BOTTOM

BOTTOM
TOP

FOLDING IN BEDS AT NEW ROAD OKEHAMPTON

The southern part of the workings is now occupied by other factories but, traced from north to south and using binoculars where access is impossible, the faces reveal a gradual change from normal symmetrical folds at the north end to more steeply overturned and thrust structures at the southern end.

If permission is obtained to visit the part still quarried, the explorer may find nodules in the beds. There is also plenty of opportunity to look for the clues which tell the geologist which was the original top and bottom of a bed. Grading in grain size is one—the larger grains are at the base of the bed and the grain size becomes finer towards the top. Another feature, found on the bottom of the bed, is the sole mark—formed by eddies in the currents which brought the material there, they look like bumps on the base of the bed. They are, in fact, thickened areas where the sands filled hollows scooped out by the eddies (Figure 50).

A more easily accessible site at which to see fold features occurs along New Road as you leave Okehampton westwards along the A30. Several small quarries were cut into the higher side of the road, again in the Crackington sandstones and shales. Figure 51 shows the first quarry, flanked by advertisement hoardings, before the 30mph limit is reached. It reveals the nose of a fold which has been almost overturned, from left to right as you view the face.

CHAPTER 12

The Tamar Valley and Its Scenery

A major river of the West Country, yet only a modest sixty miles in length by other standards, the Tamar almost completely separates Cornwall and Devon. Hence the long-standing quip that only the chains of the Torpoint ferry at Plymouth prevent Cornwall from drifting away! The Tamar valley contains a great variety of scenery and geological interest, broadly dividing into three districts. Above Launceston, it crosses the repetitive Carboniferous shales and sandstones; the central district is notable for its mining interest, and the lower valley, of course, for its splendid estuary.

The source of the Tamar must be just about the most unimpressive part of it. No tumbling brook here among rugged hills, only a tiny trickle in an insignificant depression half-a-mile east of the A39 at Woolley Barrows.

The upper Tamar is a land of ridge roads and the A39 one of the best examples. From Woolley Barrows southwards to Kilkhampton it follows the watershed between the Tamar and the short streams flowing to the north Cornwall coast. Beyond Kilkhampton its role is taken over by the B3254. The coastal rivers are short and steep and, again, roads avoid them and keep to the ridge tops. The relationship of these small valleys to the Tamar is revealed in Map 19.

The normal catchment basin of a river widens away from its source, but on the north-western side the Tamar's is clearly eaten into by this coastal drainage. Why did the Tamar not flow direct to this coast as well, since it is so near at hand and convenient?

THE REASONS FOR ITS COURSE

The order of events is again the answer. The Tamar is a very ancient river—geologists call it an antecedent river, one

MAP 19

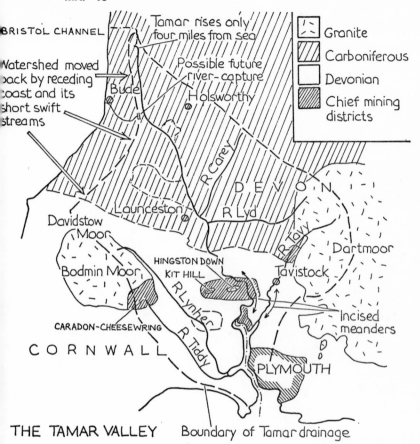

THE TAMAR VALLEY   Boundary of Tamar drainage

which has maintained its course across a later uplifting of the rocks around it.

The upper Tamar crosses an open landscape down to Launceston, but a little farther south its character changes rapidly. Greystone Bridge on the A384 marks the transformation for there the river actually passes into higher ground, its valley sides become steeper, and its loops and bends are held in Carboniferous and Devonian slates and shales until it has passed right down through the central mining district and reached its estuary south of Calstock.

This higher ground in the central district was created at the same time as the earth movements which tilted Dartmoor to the south (page 34 and Figure 6). Figure 52 shows how, towards the close of these mid-Tertiary movements, when the Alps were formed in southern Europe, the effect in south-west England changed from a tilting movement to a gentle warping. In the Tamar area the Carboniferous beds of the upper valley were warped downwards in the great synclinorium of

FIG 52

RIVER TAMAR & EARTH MOVEMENTS

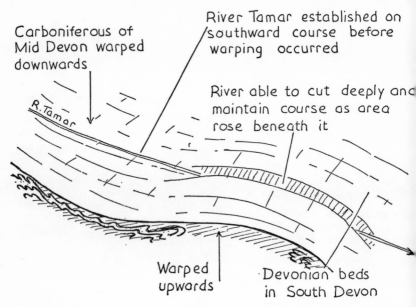

Carboniferous of Mid Devon warped downwards

River Tamar established on southward course before warping occurred

River able to cut deeply and maintain course as area rose beneath it

R. Tamar

Warped upwards

Devonian beds in South Devon

mid-Devon, while to the south the central areas rose around the river. It was rather like keeping the knife still and pushing the cake up gently from underneath. The slowness of the up-warping allowed the Tamar to maintain its route. It cut into the land, incising its meandering course as the area rose around it. So at Greystones Bridge it now seems to do the impossible and flows into and through higher ground.

Now, if the uplift had been rapid, the Tamar would have been obstructed and forced to turn aside, towards the northern coast, no doubt. The northern coast, of course, was not so near at hand in those days. Its present position is a more recent feature and, returning to Map 19, here is the explanation of the indentation into the shape of the Tamar's catchment area. The short, swift coastal streams have been able to capture part of the Tamar's upper basin and, in fact, they now threaten the Tamar itself.

Journeying along the B3254 Launceston-Kilkhampton road, stop where the old railway line passed beneath on its route to Bude. The railway used this nearly-breached point only 325ft above sea level as the easiest way over the Tamar boundary, and the small coastal stream beyond is now less than 600yd (but an unknown number of years!) from capturing the headwaters of the Tamar.

THE INCISED MEANDERS OF THE TAMAR

The Tamar is deeply cut into its central area for two reasons. As described above, it had to maintain itself while the South Devon area was warped upwards around it. A second reason was the retreat of the high sea levels of the Ice Age. Fragments of some of these old levels are well preserved in the valley; there are many pieces of the 430ft level in the Bere Alston area, for example. Each time the sea went down to a lower level the river had to cut its valley deeply to get down to the new position.

The explorer can picture the valley as once being at the level of the Hingston Down ridge with the river meandering to and fro along a fairly gentle valley floor. Then, as the need to lower its valley occurred, these bends and loops were deeply entrenched around the eastern end of the Hingston Down granite, making the wonderfully varied views seen today.

Although the steep slopes were an advantage to the mines (Chapter 13), they were anything but that to the heavy traffic of those days since the river was the main artery of trade. Transport away from the quays was faced with steep gradients up the valley sides.

The value of the Tamar valley landscape to horticulture must not be overlooked. The central district has provided good slopes facing the sun, well-placed to avoid cold night air draining down to lower levels, and sheltered from the direct effects of northerly winds coming down the valley.

Figure 53 illustrates the origin and form typical of nearly

every bend of the river from Horsebridge down to Calstock. These bends are the best incised meanders to be seen in South Devon.

FIG. 53

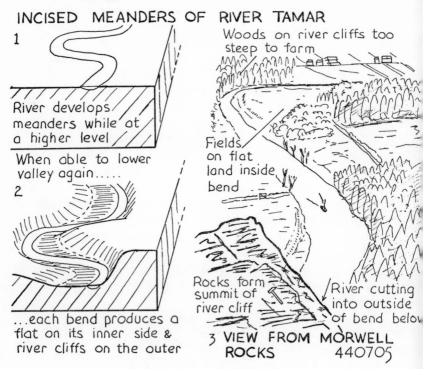

INCISED MEANDERS OF RIVER TAMAR

1

River develops meanders while at a higher level

When able to lower valley again.....

2

...each bend produces a flat on its inner side & river cliffs on the outer

Woods on river cliffs too steep to farm

Fields on flat land inside bend

Rocks form summit of river cliff

River cutting into outside of bend below

3 VIEW FROM MORWELL ROCKS   440705

HOW THE SCENERY SURVIVED

The remarkable thing about the Tamar valley's central district is its present beauty. It seems to have achieved the impossible and to have passed largely unscathed through the major copper-mining boom which took place there in the nineteenth century, thanks in no small measure to the conservation practised by the major landowners. Only Calstock suffered, the original manor falling into the hands of mining prospectors, and the slopes around Gunnislake certainly bear the worst visual scars.

Frank Booker's phrase 'the strange dichotomy' (*Industrial Archaeology of the Tamar Valley*, David & Charles, 1967) is the most apt description of this area, for in the midst of all its mines, mills and brickworks it remained a horticultural area and a tourist route for river trippers and picnic parties.

Significantly, the Duke of Bedford received over £2,000 for damage to his pheasant woods at the same time as his royalties from Devon Great Consols amounted to over £100,000! (See Map 24). So, as far as possible, mine developments were closely controlled, particularly the siting of chimneys from the flues of the arsenic and lead smelters. Getting the poisonous smoke clear of homes, gardens and livestock, a major problem in the deep valley, required long flues to hilltop chimneys from which the smoke would be dispersed by the westerly winds passing over the valley.

The close watch that was kept on developments is something to be thankful for today, for the valley contains some outstandingly beautiful scenery. The physical forms of the river, together with the human contribution to the landscape, built up on a variety of rocks, make the whole area delightful. Broad rolling ridges of farmland give way abruptly to wooded and sometimes almost vertical river-cliffs. At Morwell Rocks and opposite Gunnislake, strangely sculptured pillars rise from the steep slopes.

FIG 54

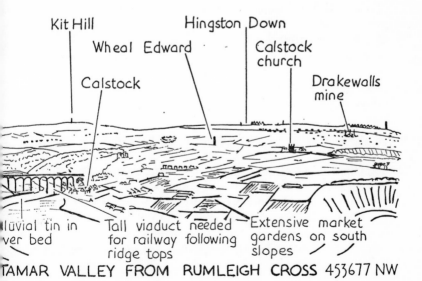

TAMAR VALLEY FROM RUMLEIGH CROSS 453677 NW

One of the most compelling features seen by the tourists is Chimney Rock opposite Gunnislake. It stands in private woodlands but can be viewed from the village or from the river boats at Weir Head. The rock is formed of hard, highly

FIG 55

CHIMNEY ROCK GUNNISLAKE 432714 E

metamorphosed slates. These slates outcrop repeatedly in similar piles as far down as Morwell Rocks, and a fine river terrace has been cut into them opposite Hatches Green; it can be seen best from the upper parts of Gunnislake. Chimney Rock itself was originally known as Sharp Tor and was renamed in the nineteenth century because of its resemblance to a mine chimney.

THE TAMAR ESTUARY

The tidal reaches of the Tamar do, of course, extend up into the central mining areas as far as Weir Head. This was important to the mines, giving direct sea access to their ports at Morwellham and Calstock. Of the major tributaries which enter the estuary, the Tavy is now tidal to the dam at Lopwell, the river Lynher to Notter Bridge and the river Tiddy to Tideford. Each tidal limit was marked by the site of a long-established bridge; New Bridge at Gunnislake and Denham

Bridge on the river Tavy lie just above tidal water, while the A38 crosses the Lynher and the Tiddy exactly at its limit.

This estuary system is known as a ria—the drowned landscape of a former river valley. The cause, as with so many landscape features of Devon and Cornwall, was the see-saw changing of sea level during the Ice Age. Almost the last event then was the rise in level known as the Flandrian transgression. It occurred about 10,000 years ago and allowed the sea to flood all the major valleys of South Devon and Cornwall, in the case of the Tamar drowning a landscape which lay some 60-80ft below the present surface of the water.

Evidence of the original depth of the valley is provided by the piers of the Tavy railway viaduct and Brunel's railway bridge at Saltash. At Tavy viaduct the rock bed lies 67ft below high water at its deepest point and at Saltash the depth is 68ft.

The contrast between this part of the Tamar and its other districts is the most noticeable of all and a river trip from Calstock to Plymouth is the best way to appreciate it. From hemmed-in bends and crags above Calstock, the slopes begin to lie farther back from the banks until, beyond Halton Quay, the landscape suddenly opens out and you are in a world where water and sky are dominant, and the gentle distant banks serve only as a boundary between the two.

FIG 56

BELOW TIDEFORD 355598 SE

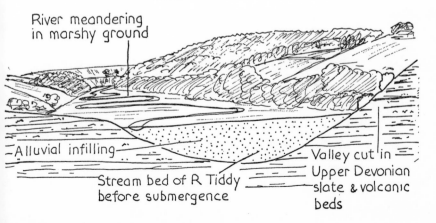

River meandering in marshy ground

Alluvial infilling

Stream bed of R Tiddy before submergence

Valley cut in Upper Devonian slate & volcanic beds

It is not an impression which will remain all the way down to the sea, of course, for at Saltash high ridges meet the river, obvious reason for siting the two bridges there.

It is when you turn away from the main river itself into the tributary valleys and smaller creeks that you realise just how much the recent submergence means in terms of landscape. In these off-shoots the channel narrows, surrounded by mud-banks and saltings, which are only part of the river at high water. In many places, the banks beyond are heavily wooded and for the naturalist there is an interesting mixture of salt-water and freshwater life, a blend somewhere between the countryside and the seashore.

MAP 20

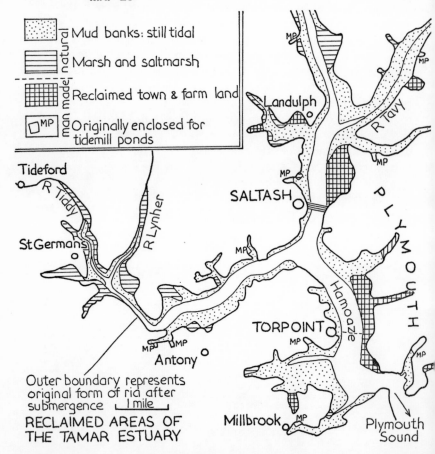

RECLAIMED AREAS OF
THE TAMAR ESTUARY

The rivers are obviously doing their best to fill the sub-merged landscape again with sediment, and the amount they have already reclaimed can be seen at many sites. The river Tiddy at Tideford—seen from the main road just east of the village—is a notable example. Old warehouses and limekilns which burned stone brought in by barge from Plymouth, remind us that the river was once navigable up to this point.

The amount of infilling which has occurred around the estuary, much of it hastened by man, is shown in Map 20 but the effects of submergence are not limited to the areas which still lie below high water. They are also evident farther up these valleys.

The reason for this can be understood when we recall the whole nature of river erosion. Throughout its course, every river has a delicate balance between its energy on the one hand and the amount of erosion and transport of material it has to do on the other. In the upper valley it usually has more energy and cuts down rapidly into the rocks—erosion is dominant. Towards the mouth of the river the situation is reversed, its energies are absorbed in carrying all the sedi-

FIG 57

RIVERS & RISING SEA-LEVEL

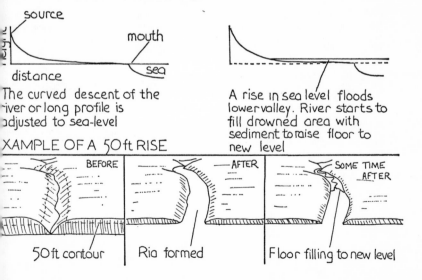

The curved descent of the river or long profile is adjusted to sea-level

A rise in sea level floods lower valley. River starts to fill drowned area with sediment to raise floor to new level

EXAMPLE OF A 50ft RISE

BEFORE — AFTER — SOME TIME AFTER

50 ft contour   Ria formed   Floor filling to new level

ment it has produced—often it cannot manage the task so deposition is dominant.

Any interference with the river can upset this balance of its activities. If sea level falls, for example, the river has to adjust its whole course to a new and lower level. To do this it must erode its lower areas instead of depositing material in them as it would normally do. If, on the other hand, the sea level rises, as it has recently, the opposite is true. The river now has to fill up its valley to get back up to the new level (Figure 57).

A journey up the Tiddy or the Lynher between Notter Bridge and Pillaton will soon prove the point. The streams are flowing within flat-floored valleys, filled with sediment they have had to dump in order to come up to the level of the submerged Tamar ria. Before the submergence they would have revealed sloping sides leading right down to the river bank.

THE CHARACTER OF THE RIVER

It would take the best part of a lifetime to know the Tamar system intimately. The Victorians were probably better acquainted with it than we are today; it featured largely in their picture postcards because of the river trips. The river was often painted, much written about and regarded by them as a romantic place. Somehow it seems to have been by-passed by the tourist trade of the twentieth century, bent on crossing the river at Plymouth or Gunnislake to go west into Cornwall. It is fortunate that this is so, for the valley is still best appreciated in small groups, its lanes unsuited to mass traffic. If its tourist use remains largely unplanned and uncommercialised, its character will be preserved and its scenic beauty will not be marred. Geological conservation often amounts to leaving things alone.

Chapter 13

The Valley and Its Mines

The Tamar mineral lodes are associated with the reappearance of granite in the central valley. Two outcrops occur, on Kit Hill and Hingston Down, and both are evidence of the hidden link between the large masses of Dartmoor and Bodmin Moor.

The Tamar has avoided the granite outcrops as far as possible, incising itself around their eastern margin. The only point where it flows over granite is south of Blanchdown Wood, the Devon Great Consols site, isolating a small area of granite on the Devon bank.

However, although the granite outcrops mainly on the Cornish bank, mineral lodes occur on both sides of the river, covering an area roughly twelve miles wide by four miles north to south. The lodes on the Devon bank are associated with elvan and felsite dykes, running east-west through heavily metamorphosed slates. Map 21 shows the boundary of the metamorphosed ground and the greater concentration of lodes within this zone is a noticeable feature.

THE NATURE OF THE MINERALISATION

Tin and copper were the predominant metals raised in the Tamar valley. The lodes are mainly east-west in trend and the ones within the metamorphic aureole were more productive than those in the granite. In the granite the lodes became thin and stringy, more like the stockworks described at Hemerdon wolfram mine (page 79). There was a good deal of wolfram present with the Tamar valley tin as well, Drakewalls and Prince of Wales mines being the largest tin producers.

Copper, and its associated arsenic, was, however, the most rewarding mineral of the area, the principal sites being Holm-

bush on the west, Hingston Down in the centre and Devon
Great Consols and Gawton to the east of the river.

Returning again to Map 21, a striking feature of the area is
the number of later north-south lodes or 'crosscourses' as the

MAP 21

miners named them. These often split the earlier east-west
deposits, affecting them in the same fashion as a tear-fault.
Miners following the deposit below ground would come to a
dead end and then have to work along the crosscourse, digging
the distance it had heaved the broken lode apart and hoping
to pick it up again on the far side.

Many of these north-south crosscourses yielded lead ores
(galena). Two cut through the Bere Alston area and each sus-
tained a line of mines, worked intermittently from medieval
times to the nineteenth century. They were noted for their

high silver content, but a small amount of silver has also been worked in the Tamar district from copper lodes, in the Silver Valley and Wheal Langford mines south of Kit Hill.

Unfortunately, the most notable crosscourse of all did not contain any lead—the one known as the Great Crosscourse, Map 21. Nevertheless, it has played an important role in the history of both the mines and the river. It split the rich copper lodes of Devon Great Consols (Chapter 14) and also split and heaved the eastern end of the granite at Gunnislake. Its presence may well have helped the Tamar to cut its course around the eastern end of the Hingston Down ridge, being one of the few north-south structures of the district.

HISTORY OF THE TAMAR MINES

Recorded mining history in the valley begins with silver-lead working at Bere Alston in the thirteenth century. The area was divided into four mining fields named South, Middle, Old and Fershull. Of these, Fershull survives today as Furzehill and the nineteenth-century stack of this mine can still be seen up the lane from Weir Quay.

MAP 22

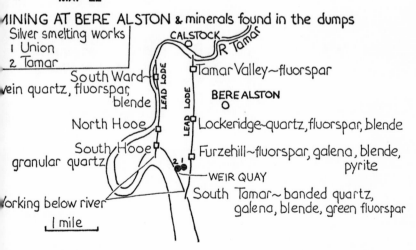

MINING AT BERE ALSTON & minerals found in the dumps

Silver smelting works
1 Union
2 Tamar

CALSTOCK
R Tamar

South Ward
vein quartz, fluorspar, blende

Tamar Valley~fluorspar

BERE ALSTON

North Hooe

LEAD LODE
LEAD LODE

Lockeridge~quartz, fluorspar, blende

South Hooe
granular quartz

Furzehill~fluorspar, galena, blende, pyrite

WEIR QUAY

Working below river

South Tamar~ banded quartz, galena, blende, green fluorspar

1 mile

The variable nature of mineral deposits was already recognised in medieval times, since the royal dues were based on production rather than a fixed annual sum. The ore was

described as having 'diversetez de bonntez et quantitez de res-
pouns'. But one charge reveals that the nature of mineral
deposition was not understood in those times—tithes had
to be paid on the lead for it was regarded as a crop which
grew again !

Water was the problem of all early mining and restricted
the depths of working. In wet winters it might prevent work
altogether and the details of the number of hands employed
from week to week to do baling-out are ample meteorological
records in themselves.

The first improvements to mine drainage were probably
made in this area, records referring to the introduction of
avidods, dug by special gangs paid at the rate of £12 10s a
year. Avidods were the horizontal tunnels or adits and their
use at Bere Alston soon raised production and enabled winter
working. Driven in from the river bank they gave natural
drainage to all workings at higher levels in the hill above
and became an integral part of all later mining activity in the
South West.

The silver-lead ore was smelted in rough structures rather
like limekilns and each lode produced 3½ft of silver-lead (a
foot weighed 70lb and yielded 2dwt of silver per lb).

There is no visual evidence of this early mining left today.
The silver-lead deposits were worked off and on up to the
nineteenth century, but the gaunt chimneys and dumps of
the Tamar landscape are all of eighteenth or nineteenth
century date, mainly ruins left by another great upsurge of
activity associated with copper, tin and arsenic.

While the medieval tin mining began on Dartmoor and
moved west into Cornwall, copper working of later centuries
commenced in Cornwall and spread eastwards into Devon.
The years 1844 to 1890 were the great period of copper prosperity in the Tamar valley; the population of the mining
villages soared, the river became a highway of movement and
the valley lived and thought copper, sending its produce away
to South Wales for smelting. The activity of the last century
produced the dumps sought by mineral collectors today.

THE ROLE OF THE RIVER

Throughout this copper boom the river played a key role.

It was a source of power in an area with no coal, the usual handmaid of all heavy industry. It was a transport lifeline for the cheap movement of bulky goods and equipment, and the very nature of its landscape helped the miners' task far below the surface.

The deeply-cut meanders of the Tamar gave the valley a strongly contrasting relief. Only on the inner margins of the bends do the banks rise gently away from the river. Elsewhere the slopes are generally precipitous, leading up to broad gentle ridges above. The deep-cut valley was, therefore, ideal for adit development. Tunnels driven in at river bank level gave natural drainage to all the high ground above, sometimes as much as 500ft of hill could be unwatered in this fashion.

FIG 58

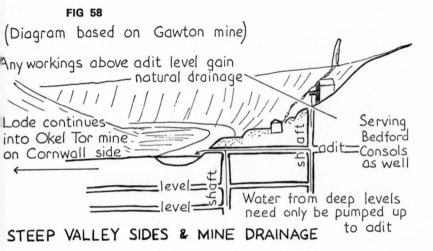

(Diagram based on Gawton mine)

Any workings above adit level gain
— natural drainage

Lode continues
into Okel Tor mine
on Cornwall side

Serving
Bedford
adit Consols
as well

level

level

Water from deep levels
need only be pumped up
to adit

STEEP VALLEY SIDES & MINE DRAINAGE

The natural drainage of upper areas of mines was most valuable in saving pumping costs; the water from deeper levels had only to be pumped up to the adit instead of to the shaft head higher up on the hill top. However, few working levels benefited directly from adits since the bulk of the deposits lay deeper than river level anyway.

If the depth of the valley helped the mines in this respect, however, in another it was a hindrance, for transport of heavy goods was a problem away from the river itself. The solution on the Cornwall bank was the East Cornwall Mineral Railway, rising from the quays at Calstock by an incline of which

K

a great deal can still be seen. On the Devon bank the problem was tackled in a way which has much more appeal to the geologist, by means of a canal which involved a two-mile tunnel beneath Morwell Down. The Tavistock canal tunnel was, like any adit, an excellent means of testing untried ground. Boring across country north-south you might cut a number of new east-west tin and copper lodes. Unfortunately, the ground beneath Morwell Down was less mineralised than had been hoped and the canal tunnel (completed in 1817) only located Wheal Crebor, the mine near its northern end.

THE MINING ECONOMY

The Tamar valley is a good example of the influence of social and economic factors on a landscape, and the explorer must remember that much of the present scenery has more than physical or geological origins. Land ownership was a major influence here—the Abbots of Tavistock and the Dukes of Bedford who followed them, together with other major landowners of the valley like the Earl of Mount Edgecumbe, were all interested in farming the land and good husbandry. Despite the income derived from their mines, the Dukes of Bedford regarded them as a nuisance and exercised a very close scrutiny over their development, often at great inconvenience and hardship to the community in those days. In the present century we can only be thankful to them for having preserved the attractions of the area.

The mining economy of the Tamar, being a nineteenth-century boom, was controlled by stock markets and companies to a greater extent than usual. Most Westcountry mining had been developed by groups of adventurers, using the old cost-book system of management. So the wealth of the Tamar flowed out of the valley without even the endowment of a single school or hospital to mark its passing. The busy independent community, owing little to and taking little from the large port of Plymouth at the river mouth, could only continue its high level of activity as long as there were minerals still to be won from the ground beneath it.

Another reason for the preservation of the scenery was, of course, the absence of coal. Again, the disadvantages of one century can be seen as blessings by another, for without coal

FIG 59

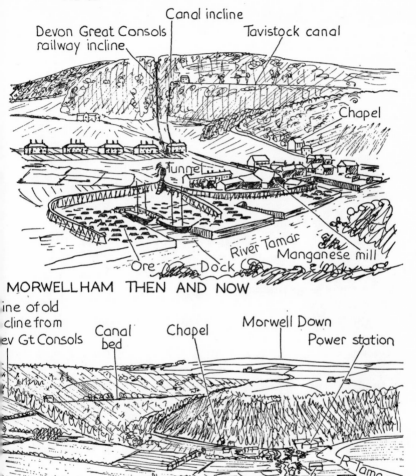

Devon Great Consols railway incline

Canal incline

Tavistock canal

Chapel

Tunnel

River Tamar

Manganese mill

Ore Dock

MORWELLHAM THEN AND NOW

ine of old cline from ev Gt Consols

Canal bed

Chapel

Morwell Down

Power station

Tamar

Manganese mill

Dock

the copper had to be sent to South Wales for smelting, thus assuring an absence of unsightly slag heaps along the Tamar.

It is easy to get romantic about the Tamar scenery now that the valley has returned to its agricultural and forestry economy—the Victorians even managed to be when the mines were active. The crowded little cottages at Calstock and above Gunnislake look neat and trim now with their colour-washed walls, but when the mines were active many of these modern homes made two or more. People lived cramped, insanitary lives with next to nothing in medical services and frequent cholera outbreaks. And as the mines boomed a population explosion occurred, with all its attendant problems.

MANGANESE MINING

This aspect of mining in the valley deserves special mention here rather than in the chapters which follow. Interesting geologically, the manganese mines have left fewer traces in the landscape than any others. The more prominent tin and copper sites are dealt with in Chapters 14 and 15.

The upper Tamar, as described in Chapter 12, crosses a little varied expanse of Carboniferous shales and sandstones. The monotonous nature of these beds at Okehampton has already been mentioned, but the southern part of the Carboniferous is broken by a number of chert outcrops. These belong to the Lower Carboniferous and are the equivalent of the Meldon Cherts (page 121).

The chert outcrops run roughly east-west along the ridges around Launceston. Crossing the river Tamar, they become more extensive between Milton Abbot and Lifton and eventually reach the Meldon area and the margins of Dartmoor.

A large number of manganese mines have been worked in the chert beds. They were developed both east and west of the Tamar but were most numerous on the east side between Milton Abbot and Lifton. This is the third mining district of the Tamar Valley, after the Kit Hill-Hingston Down and the Bere Alston districts. Map 23 shows the distribution of the manganese working sites.

Although there were several mines, none was a very large venture but they did, nevertheless, supply all the national needs for manganese for a period. Thomas Newman's *History of Coryton* states that most of them were discovered when farmers were ploughing and draining their land. The most important one was undoubtedly the Chillaton-Hogstor mine, which had several shafts and adits in the little valley flowing down through Chillaton to the river Lew. But, like nearly all these mine sites, there is very little dump material to search over for black manganese and, indeed, at Allerford

MAP 23
(Generalised from maps of the Institute of Geological Sciences with permission of the Director)

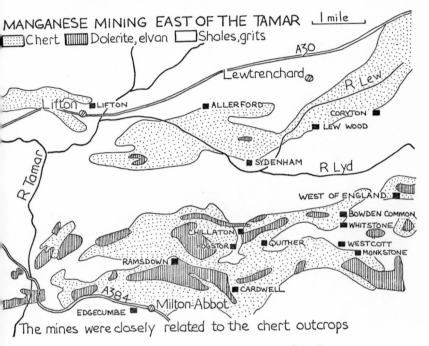

MANGANESE MINING EAST OF THE TAMAR ⎣1 mile⎦
▦Chert ▥Dolerite, elvan ☐Shales, grits

The mines were closely related to the chert outcrops

and Wolladon it is hard to find any indications of mining at all now. The geological interest is therefore an historical one, while industrial archaeologists will be familiar with the mill for grinding manganese which stands at Morwellham (Figure 59). This was the port through which the ore was exported.

The manganese did not occur in true lodes. It was probably derived from solutions which migrated into the chert beds with the numerous greenstone or dolerite intrusions. Sheet 337 of the Geological Survey gives a very accurate picture of the close association of the cherts, dolerites and manganese mining, although its interpretation of the surrounding Carboniferous and Devonian beds will probably be revised when a new survey is made. The underground development of the mines generally followed the northerly dip of the chert beds.

FIG 60

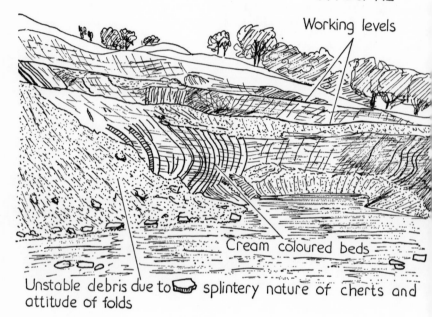

QUARRY IN MELDON CHERTS : BURLEY DOWN
497867 NE

Working levels

Cream coloured beds

Unstable debris due to splintery nature of cherts and attitude of folds

There were also some efforts to work the dolerites of the district since they have often been decomposed into ochre material, but this was never very successful because it was difficult to sort out the impurities caused by black manganese stains.

If you decide to explore the old manganese working district, it is worthwhile visiting the Forestry Commission's quarry on Burley Down, 496868 (Figure 60). Here the cherts are being worked for road metal and the quarry makes a prominent creamy gash in the hillside. It is particularly noticeable in distant views from the A386 over Black Down, lying away to the north-west as you stand at the same vantage point as that used for Figure 18.

CHAPTER 14

Tavistock and the East Bank

As a boom town Tavistock has one of the longest histories of any place in Devon. Its first prosperity was due to the Dartmoor tin streaming when, as a stannary town, tin was brought there to be 'coigned'—a piece broken off the corner of each ingot for assaying the content—and stamped. When the tin-mining industry exhausted most of the Dartmoor gravels and moved west into Cornwall, Tavistock was left in a depressed condition. It revived again under the impetus of the wool trade but might have received a second setback after that had it not been quickly caught up in the nineteenth-century West Devon copper boom.

Evidence of the prosperity which the copper mines once brought to it is everywhere : the canal, buildings which housed foundries, and neat rows of miners' cottages at sites like Parkwood and Westbridge. These cottages were erected by the Duke of Bedford, and their distinctive architecture can be recognised in groups all over the district. But the most notable of his building achievements in Tavistock must surely be the renewed use of the local Hurdwick Stone.

THE HURDWICK FREESTONE

In appearance, Tavistock is perhaps the most geologically satisfying town in Devon. The broad Plymouth road, square and public buildings, the market and Fitzford church were all laid out by the duke, financed no doubt by his royalties from the mines. Today they are outstanding because of the unique green colour, attractively set off by granite mouldings and dressings. How pleasant it is to stand near the Bedford Hotel and look across the square when the mid-day sun is full on the walls.

The green Hurdwick Stone is a volcanic ash and close inspection of the walls reveals its tiny air cavities. It is a free-stone, sufficiently compact to cut well and weather satisfactor-ily. The main quarry lies to the north of the town, 474766, about 180yd east of the Brentor road. It was worked for the

FIG 61

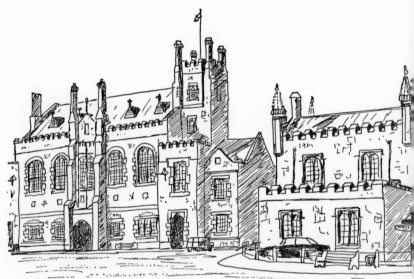

BUILDINGS IN HURDWICK STONE : TAVISTOCK 483745

building of Tavistock Abbey and, at the Dissolution, destruc-tion of the Abbey buildings provided a lot of stone for re-use in the town without resort to the quarry. A parallel case occurred with the limestones at Buckfastleigh (*Geology Explained in South and East Devon*, pp 79-80). The quarry went out of use again after the nineteenth-century working and today it seems a strangely small depression to have pro-duced so much beautiful stone. Its site is now devoted to farming use but the stone is still worked, mainly for repair work, at another small quarry by the old Tavistock workhouse.

DEVON GREAT CONSOLS

It was this mine above all which contributed to the pros-perity and rebuilding of Tavistock. Opened in Blanchdown

Wood overlooking the Tamar in November 1844, it grew to
fantastic richness and to final decline within sixty years.

Figure 62 shows the geology of the mine, a major producer
even by world standards. There were three principal lodes
and work began in an old pit on the north-west part of the
site. Only a few fathoms digging brought the miners on to the
back of a fabulous copper lode. As the miners traced it eastwards, however, they came up against a classic example of the
later N-S joints or crosscourses. These commonly 'heaved' or
split the earlier E-W lodes as they passed through them, producing the same horizontal displacement as a tear-fault.

FIG 62

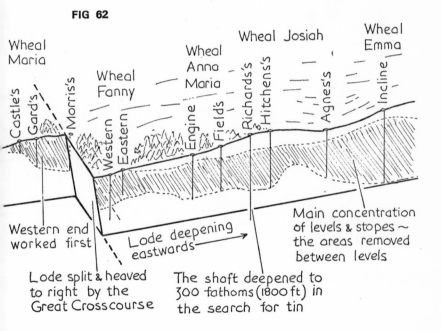

MAIN LODE AT DEVON GREAT CONSOLS

Known as the Great Crosscourse, it moved the lode on the
far side 750ft farther south but the miners soon found it again
and it was eventually proved to extend eastwards for over two
miles. The mine also included two other important lodes to
the south of Main Lode.

The mine was exceptionally rich. Copper normally occurs

in concentrations around 9 per cent and must be refined before transport, otherwise a lot of waste cargo would be carried. Lead, as a comparison, has concentrations of 70 to 80 per cent. At Devon Great Consols the copper reached 17 per cent, nearly double normal values and the lodes were up to 30ft wide ! The ore was chalcopyrite, with pyrite, quartz and fluorspar.

In the original part of the mine the ore was only 100ft below ground but, as Figure 62 shows, eastwards it became deeper. This was not simply because the eastern shafts started from greater heights above the river. The ore body also divided eastwards, including a barren zone between its higher and lower tongues.

The deepest shaft in the mine was Richards's in Wheal Josiah. It reached 1,800ft, or 300 fathoms in mining terms. The copper in Wheal Josiah lay 50-115 fathoms down and the extra depth was the result of the duke's insistence on a search for tin below. The experience of Dolcoath mine in Cornwall led his advisers to believe that a rich mine like Devon Great Consols must also contain tin at depth. Unfortunately it did not and when Richards's shaft had reached 300 fathoms the search was abandoned.

Devon Great Consols mine, which can only be visited by permission, is reached by turning off the main Tavistock-Gunnislake road at Gulworthy. Its huge dumps dominate the hillside as the road descends beyond Gulworthy into the Tamar Valley, and they remain bare of vegetation still because of the arsenic present in them.

Like most copper mines, Devon Great Consols turned to arsenic to boost its later years and between 1868 and 1902 its works calcined 600,000 tons of arsenopyrite, yielding 72,000 tons of refined arsenic. The huge arsenic works, covering eight acres and with seven calciners and nearly 5,500ft of flues, is the dominant relic among the dumps, with the tall chimney at the top of the slope.

The dumps have of course been worked over several times by smaller concerns and it is true to say of most mine sites that the present layout is hardly any guide to the appearance of the place at the time of the original closure. Work continues today with small leaching plants and there are proposals to begin fluorspar extraction, now a very marketable product.

The fluorspar is glassy, transparent or transluscent, and ranges from white to pale greens and blues in colour. It was a favourite ornamental stone in Victorian times although

FIG 63

ARSENIC LABYRINTH AT DEVON GREAT CONSOLS

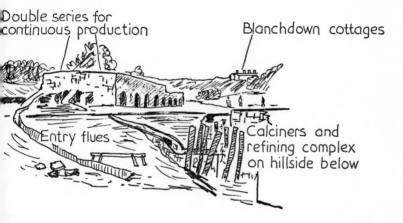

Double series for continuous production

Blanchdown cottages

Entry flues

Calciners and refining complex on hillside below

Parts of the process

An Oxland rotary calciner

Milling the white powder

Scarf to safeguard breathing

Millstones housed exactly as in watermills

Devon Great Consols never yielded that quality. It is used as a flux in steel manufacture, where it is better than the limestone used originally; in making hydro-fluoric acid for insecticides, dyestuffs and preservatives, and also for ceramic and enamel coatings.

THE ARSENIC INDUSTRY

After 1870 the Tamar valley became the world's largest arsenic producing area. As arsenopyrite (arsenical iron pyrites), the mineral occurred in the copper lodes there in unusually large quantities. It is heavy, light grey in colour and metallic in appearance. After striking it hard with a hammer, sniff it quickly and it will smell like garlic—this rather unusual geological technique is harmless as it needs one-sixth of a teaspoonful of pure refined arsenic to kill a man!

At first the arsenopyrite was regarded as a nuisance and thrown on the dumps when copper was king. But falling profits caused the mines to think again and the great plants at Devon Great Consols, Devon Friendship and Gawton are evidence of their eventual dependence on arsenic production.

FIG 64

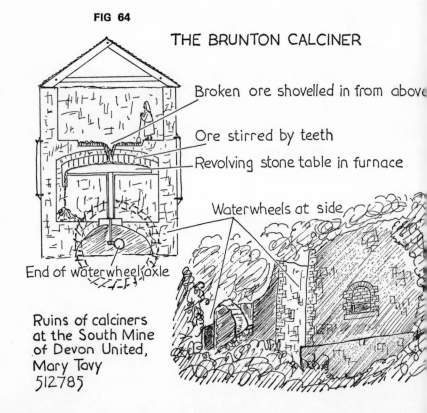

THE BRUNTON CALCINER

Broken ore shovelled in from above

Ore stirred by teeth

Revolving stone table in furnace

Waterwheels at side

End of waterwheel axle

Ruins of calciners at the South Mine of Devon United, Mary Tavy 512785

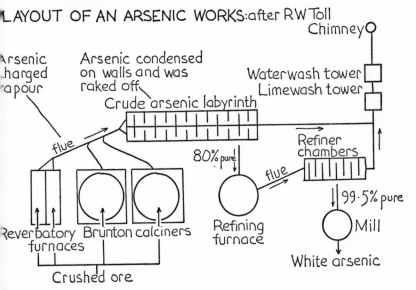

FIG 65

LAYOUT OF AN ARSENIC WORKS: after R W Toll

There was a slump in 1900 when prices fell to £10 a ton and, while the first world war brought brief revival in hopes, there has been no arsenic production locally since 1925.

The arsenic industry worked in the usual fashion of the mines, washing, sorting and crushing being the first process, with the ore then classified for treatment as pure or impure. The pure ore was roasted in calciners, of either the Brunton or Oxland type. The Brunton calciner was the more common and the square remains of them can be seen at Devon Great Consols, at Devon Friendship at Mary Tavy, and at Devon United across the river there. If you go right down to the bottom of Marytavy, cross the footbridge and turn up the east bank of the river, the first feature encountered at the South Mine of Devon United is a Pelton wheel, but higher up the bank are two Brunton calciners and an arsenic labyrinth. From above you can look into the calciners and see the circular fire-brick-lined roasting chamber. It contained a circular brick-bed, with a sloping upper surface like a very shallow cone. The whole bed was mounted on an iron plate so that it could be revolved by a waterwheel. The wheel pits can be seen along-side at Devon United.

The ore was fed into the centre from a room above and moved down over the brick bed. Stirred by obliquely set teeth and roasted by the furnace beneath the table, it was completely calcined. There is an interesting picture of the Devon United site in its active days in *Historic Mining Scenes at Surface* (D. B. Barton, Truro).

The Oxland calciner was quite different—a firebrick-lined tube, 5ft in diameter and over 40ft long. It was mounted at a low angle and rotated slowly so that the ore gradually worked its way down to the lower end. This was a very dirty process though, the rotation increased the amount of dangerous soot produced and so it was less commonly used despite the saving in fuel.

One way of treating impure ore was to roast it with salt to form copper chloride—hence the name of another process used, the chlorination method.

Figure 65 shows the general arrangement of an arsenic

MAP 24

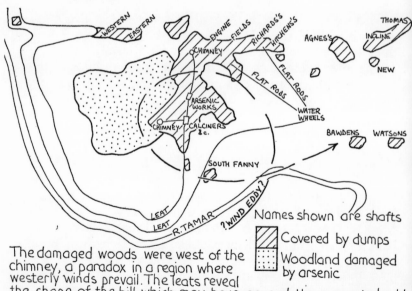

The damaged woods were west of the chimney, a paradox in a region where westerly winds prevail. The leats reveal the shape of the hill which may have caused the suggested eddy

Names shown are shafts

Covered by dumps

Woodland damaged by arsenic

LATE NINETEENTH CENTURY DAMAGE Devon Gt Consols

works. The most common remain found on the sites now, apart from the base of the calciners, is nearly always the labyrinth where the vapours were condensed and the grey 'flowers of arsenic' grew, to await the men who would come and rake them out. At Devon Great Consols, the labyrinth still retains its roof in parts. It has the usual two sets of chambers to enable extraction to go on in one while condensing continued in the other. Refining was necessary in a second series of chambers to bring the final product to a 99.5 per cent purity.

Limestone baffles and a water-wash tower in the final flue to the chimney reduced the eventual arsenic discharge to as little as 0.1gr of arsenic and 1.5gr of sulphur dioxide per cubic foot of flue gas, but as Map 24 shows it was still enough to do great damage to life nearby and to smell most unpleasantly. The Duke of Bedford received £2,024 for such damage to his pheasant wood apart from his dues as mine landlord!

GAWTON MINE

Of the other mines in the valley Gawton is well worth a visit. It is reached by the track from Gawton Farm and was another major arsenic producer. Its dumps are believed to total a quarter of a million tons and the higher ones are distinctive because of their brown sandy nature. Barren because they still contain much arsenic, the lack of plant cover allows the rain to sculpture fantastic shapes in them in places.

But the chief interest here lies down by the river. Passing the range of ruined furnaces and the beginning of the great arsenic flue which leads to the twisted chimney high above, go down to the limekilns. These are massive remains of economic geology and agricultural history for they burned Middle Devonian limestones brought up from Plymouth by barge. Kilns existed at all the Tamar quays and supplied lime to the local farms.

Beyond the kilns there is an unusual sight—a brilliant green stream bed. Water draining from the Gawton workings flows across the track leading to the lowest dumps and it is so charged with mineral solution that it has coated all its bed with green copper minerals. Wheal Emma, near Buckfastleigh, has another example of this phenomenon. But, it must be stressed here, photographs are better than hammers! The hammer can be used on the dumps beyond where brass-coloured crystals of iron pyrite can be found, golden-coloured chalcopyrite (copper) and grey arsenopyrite (arsenic). The reddish appearance of the Gawton rock waste shows that it is not fresh. The dumps are burnt residues, heavily stained with iron oxide.

FIG 66

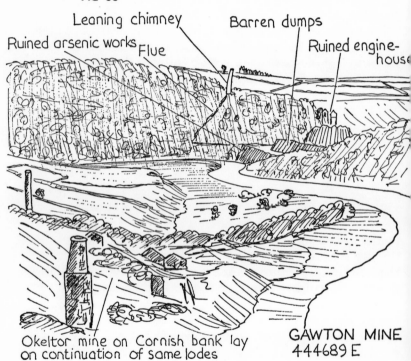

Leaning chimney

Barren dumps

Ruined arsenic works

Flue

Ruined engine-house

Okeltor mine on Cornish bank lay on continuation of same lodes

GAWTON MINE
444689 E

THE SILVER LEAD MINES

The Bere Alston silver mines have the longest history of any in the valley—a history of times of bonanza production alternating with dismally low returns. They were first worked in the thirteenth century and Bere Alston itself was founded as a mining settlement. Tithes had then to be paid on the lead but, as might be expected, the rector of Bere Ferrers had no use for it and sold it back to the miners at 2s a load.

Geologically speaking, the value of the silver dropped with depth. Occasionally, the upper parts of the two lodes produced 170oz of silver per ton of lead, but lower down it was only 30oz. Nevertheless, this was much better than the 8-9oz per ton obtained at Wheal Betsy, near Mary Tavy. The Bere Alston lodes also contained blende (zinc), green fluorspar, and vast quantities of banded quartz. With small samples of the galena (lead), these are the minerals to be found on the dumps of the area today, eg South Tamar or Cleave mine, down river from Weir Quay. Permission to visit the latter must be obtained from Cleave Farm.

Most of the lead mines worked ground beneath the valley sides, the lodes dipping eastwards, but because of the course of the river the mines at the southern ends of the lodes, South Hooe and South Tamar, had workings beneath the river bed, (Map 22). At South Hooe, the lode ran out beneath a great bend in the river which made pumping from its lower levels a problem—solved eventually by putting in an underground engine.

South Tamar's working life was ended by the river in 1856, when it broke into the levels through the collapse of a more clayey bed within the local slates, a feature known to miners as a 'slide'. Considerable amounts of silver-lead remain in its workings but no way of retrieving them has yet been discovered.

L

CHAPTER 15

The West Side of the Tamar

Since the watershed of the Tamar with the north coast streams has already been described in Chapter 12, the districts dealt with now lie south of Davidstow. With nearly thirty miles to cover, even as the crow flies, from Davidstow to the Tamar's mouth, the explorer is bound to divide the country into convenient units to study and the first ones dealt with here concern the eastern margins of Bodmin Moor.

If the traveller passes along the A395 Launceston–Camelford road until Hallworthy, and then turns off along the B3262 to the old Otterham railway station he will, broadly speaking, have Carboniferous beds to the north and Upper Devonian to the south. The Upper Devonian outcrops form an extensive level around this part of Bodmin Moor, despite the fact that they are varied by thrust faults. The thrusts have created outcrops of Lower Carboniferous slates, sheared lavas and tuffs—outliers among the Upper Devonian—and these reach their greatest width of outcrop around Davidstow.

In the Carboniferous country to the north, examine the Boscastle one-inch Geological Survey map between Otterham and Wainhouse Corner, and again, from Wainhouse Corner out to the coast near Chipman Strand. Here on the Tamar watershed and its subsidiary ridges the density of faults recorded is much less than in the valleys towards the coast. It suggests that the ridges have survived because they were much less faulted, but it is also likely evidence of the greater difficulty in tracing fault structures over featureless ridges with few exposures, compared to mapping them in deeply-cut valley sides and stream beds.

Davidstow Moor, straddling the watershed between the Tamar's tributary river, the Inny, and the river Camel to the west, is a well-developed example of the 1,000ft surface. Already described on Dartmoor, the 1,000ft is the best of the

MAP 25

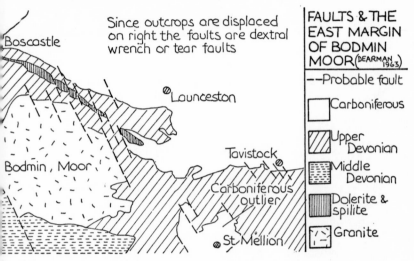

Since outcrops are displaced on right the faults are dextral wrench or tear faults

FAULTS & THE EAST MARGIN OF BODMIN MOOR (DEARMAN 1963)

--Probable fault

☐ Carboniferous

▨ Upper Devonian

▦ Middle Devonian

▥ Dolerite & spilite

⬚ Granite

Boscastle
Launceston
Tavistock
Bodmin , Moor
Carboniferous outlier
St. Mellion

Westcountry's higher surfaces, developed under land conditions in late Tertiary times.

THE MARGIN OF BODMIN MOOR

By a curious coincidence the north-west margin of Bodmin Moor is strongly affected by Tertiary tear-faults in similar fashion to north-east Dartmoor. At least two occur along the eastern margin where the granite itself has a remarkably straight boundary. As the granite boundary begins to swing round north-westwards towards Camelford it becomes step-like, the result of several more NW-SE faults (Map 25).

The river Lynher follows the eastern boundary of the Bodmin granite very closely, passing through a narrow belt of metamorphosed Upper Devonian rocks and granite intrusions down to Rilla Mill. West of Rilla Mill these aureole rocks form a large, irregular and much-faulted embayment in the granite margin.

MINIONS AND THE CHEESEWRING

This south-east corner of Bodmin Moor was heavily mineralised with tin and copper lodes. At Minions there is a large, ruined engine-house to the north. Leaving this to the left, follow the track of the old tramway up to the Phoenix United mine sett and the Cheesewring quarry.

The tramway ran into the quarry which reveals a grey, hard, well-jointed stone, the joints being fresher near the base of the working. Near local mineral lodes, the granite is softer and discoloured by iron. A wolfram lode from the Phoenix United mines sett is exposed in the quarry.

FIG 67

TOR FORMATIONS ON BODMIN MOOR

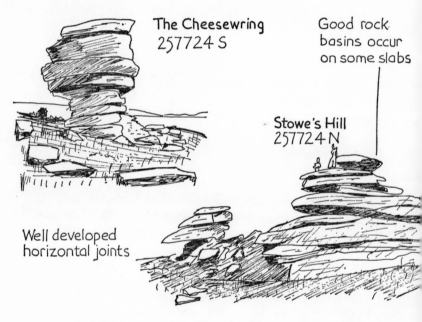

Leaving the quarry, make for the Cheesewring itself on the hill above. Figure 67 shows two views of this unusual group of tors, which look rather like weather-beaten men wearing cloth caps. Regularly-spaced horizontal joints have been important in their formation and on several slabs there are good examples of rock basins.

From the hill-top, the view to the south-east reveals the abandoned mining landscape of Phoenix United, with gaunt walls rising among the widespread dumps, and the comparatively well-preserved stack and engine-house of the Prince of Wales Shaft. This shaft, 17ft square, was begun in 1907, the last attempt to work the mine. By 1913 it was 1,200ft deep. There the lode was 20ft wide but, unfortunately, unproductive. The project was abandoned but the house and its 80in engine were kept in order until the 1930s. In its earlier workings the sett had yielded over 80,000 tons of 6 per cent copper ore and 16,000 tons of tin.

The Phoenix United dumps can occupy several days of diligent searching. The mine had a very diverse group of minerals in it. Apart from the more easily obtainable quartz, chalcopyrite and green-coloured secondary copper ores, there are rare treasures to be had occasionally. The brown, branch-like, native copper is one. Others which occur are Andrewsite (bluish green, globular disks) and chalcosiderite, the blackish-green iron mineral, a clay ironstone with some additional copper.

MAP 26

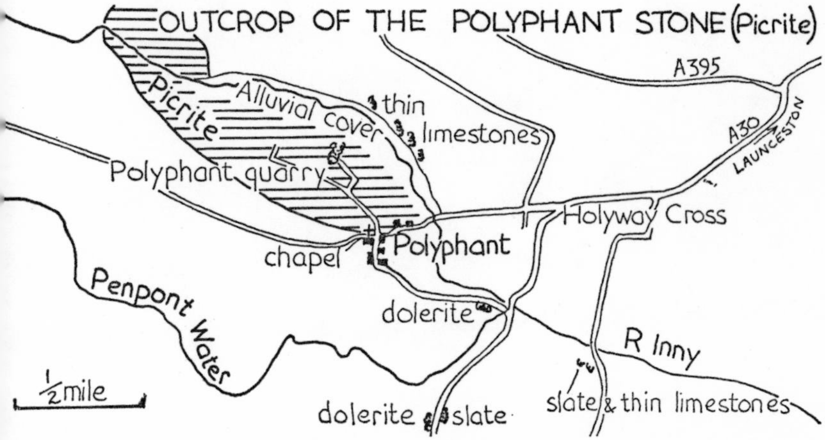

The boundary of the Tamar valley drainage runs west of the Cheesewring and through Minions to Caradon Hill and Tokenbury Corner. Mining enthusiasts will doubtless continue their walks over the watershed and down the gully to Gona-mena and Darite where the site of the famous South Caradon copper mine stands. Worked 1833-90, it was the third largest copper producer in the Westcountry.

Moving away from Bodmin Moor, the B3254 can be taken towards Launceston, turning off at Congdon's Shop to pass through Lewannick and reach Polyphant.

POLYPHANT STONE

Outcropping near the village of the same name, south-west of Launceston, Polyphant Stone is certainly the most famous in the western Tamar valley. It occurs on both banks of the

FIG 68

Large blocks of rotted picrite in disused face

POLYPHANT QUARRY 257827

The three joint planes allowed large blocks to be won

river Inny, the major area being south of the river, with a smaller outcrop in Lezant parish, south of Trekelland.

Polyphant Stone is properly described as a serpentinised picrite. The name picrite means bitter rock, a label earned for it through its high magnesium content. It is generally grey-green in colour with large white oval specks. Hand specimens have a soapy feel when polished, and it is the ability of this rock to take a polish and to be carved which has made it famous. The stone was first worked in the eleventh century and finished slabs have a marble-like appearance.

The large quarry, worked until the early twentieth century, lies north of the village. Follow the lane up to the Chapel and then take the track beside it. The track curves round to the north-west and in the third field another rougher track branches off down to the quarry. Crags of picrite outcrop all the way down the slopes.

The rock is badly decomposed in both crags and quarry and in the latter it is hard to get a fresh specimen. Figure 68 shows the three sets of joints which cleave the rock and made it possible, despite blasting, to win large blocks from the face. The blocks were sounded for weaknesses after blasting since only perfectly sound ones were of any use for ornamental carving.

Picrite is not a good external stone, it peels off in layers badly (exfoliates) and a lot of stone in Launceston, re-used from the old priory building there, provides evidence of this. It was, therefore, a favourite stone for internal work. The piers of Bratton Clovelly church and the four westernmost bays of the south arcade at Sampford Courteney church are made of it and so is the tomb of Archbishop Temple in Canterbury Cathedral. It was also used in Exeter and Truro Cathedrals. In 1911 the quarry was producing about 500 tons of finished stone per year.

The most peculiar feature of Polyphant stone is the occurrence of spheroidal masses in it, varying from 1-4ft in diameter. Cut into two, the inner concentric layers were removed leaving outer shells which made admirable basins and fonts. There is one in Launceston Roman Catholic church.

LAUNCESTON

If the Devonian and Carboniferous beds along the margin of Bodmin Moor appear to sweep up to the north-west because of the tear-faulting in the area, at Launceston at least the explorer returns to the generally east-west structures of the

Tamar Valley. The Tamar itself passes a mile east of Launceston which really stand in the vale of the river Kensey.

The geological succession around Launceston is :

Upper Carboniferous	Trebursye Beds	
Lower Carboniferous	Cannapark limestone and Barracados Cherts	Limestones Cherts
	Yeolmbridge Beds	Slates, sandstones and limestones
	NOTE : NO UNCONFORMITY	
Upper Devonian	Stourscombe Beds	Nodular, thin-bedded slates, occasionally rich in ammonoids and trilobites
	Petherwin Beds	Slates and thin limestones

The sediments continue from Devonian to Carboniferous without any break in time leading to the formation of an unconformity.

It is not possible to see good exposures of all the beds in the succession. Some are only seen in very small, overgrown quarries, not easily accessible to visitors, but there are a few larger workings in the area. These were developed in the better slates, in the small but valuable patches of limestone, or in the cherts for road metal.

Three small quarries, one since partly-filled with refuse, provide exposures of the Petherwin Beds in the lane leading from Landlake (east of South Petherwin) to Launceston. Slates outcrop in the Gatepost Quarry (326821) and limestones and slates again at the bottom of the hill (328823 and 328824) near the Lowley Brook.

A little further up the Lowley Brook, beside the South Petherwin–Launceston road, stands the Bangor Cornish Slate quarry, where evenly-bedded slates belonging to the Yeolmbridge Beds were worked. The quarry became partly flooded after closure, but the nature of the bedding is still evident in the upper faces. The Yeolmbridge Beds are also exposed in the disused Yeolmbridge slate quarry where limestone is seen on the north side, and specimens of *Gattendorfia,* a zone fossil of the Lower Carboniferous, have been found in rottenstone bands.

Passing into Launceston, the explorer reaches the lava-capped ridge which forms the site of the town and the south side of the Kensey valley. The castle is founded on these lavas which are highly vesicular, filled with cavities left by escaping gases. They are pillow lavas, deposited in submarine conditions from sea-bed eruptions. As the lava was extruded it broke away in lumps. Falling to the sea bed while still soft, it lay in heaps exactly like a pile of pillows, hence the name. There the lava cooled and solidified, with typical convex upper surfaces and concave lower ones. These can be a useful guide in trying to tell whether the beds are still the same way up or have been overturned by later folding.

Looking across the steep-sided valley of the Kensey, the opposite slopes are cut in black shales and grits, crowned by a chert ridge beyond St Stephens. St Stephens stands on one of the more prominent beds of grits—it can be traced westwards for nearly a mile, forming a noticeable terrace on the hillside.

Crossing the valley, take the old road up to St Stephens. The newer turnpike road to the east has easier gradients but fewer exposures of the black shales. Just north of St Stephens the chert ridge has been worked in the Barracados quarry (323823).

Another spot to make for near Launceston is Polson Bridge on the A30; parking is very awkward near the bridge so walk to it for a view of the mature nature of the Tamar at this point. There is a good view to the west (Figure 69) of the commanding position of Launceston. The Tamar continues through open country down to the next bridge, Greystone.

Travellers from Launceston to Tavistock will see the marked change in its nature which occurs at Greystone, described in Chapter 12. Beyond the bridge the road has to twist steeply up wooded hillsides to gain the ridge level at Dunterton.

Greystone Bridge marks the point where a number of chert and dolerite outcrops cross the river, and the dolerites are being worked at present in Greystone quarry on the Launceston side of the river. Dolerites make good, hard-wearing road gravels.

FIG 69

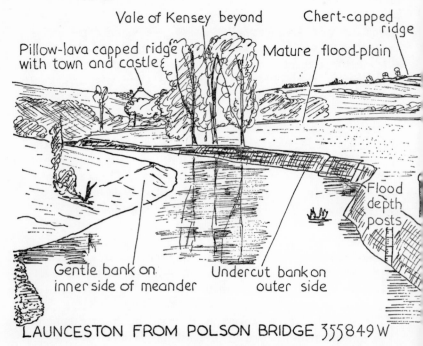

Vale of Kensey beyond

Chert-capped ridge

Pillow-lava capped ridge with town and castle

Mature flood-plain

Flood depth posts

Gentle bank on inner side of meander

Undercut bank on outer side

LAUNCESTON FROM POLSON BRIDGE 355849 W

Those who intend to keep west of the river will, however, take the Launceston–Callington road, heading for the granite outcrops of Kit Hill and Hingston Down.

THE TAMAR GRANITE OUTCROPS

Although the present Survey map shows two granite outcrops, seismic surveys indicate that there are in fact three masses here and that the Gunnislake granite is separated from the Hingston Down outcrop by an interval of metamorphosed country rock—the Great Crosscourse (Chapter 14) must pass through this zone.

The Gunnislake granite is also rather different in composition, being low in magnesium and iron. Hingston Down and Kit Hill granite is the more normal Cornish granite, fine-grained porphyritic, though there are fewer large felspars than usual.

The granite outcrops represent humps or cupolas on a buried

ridge. However, the link between the Kit Hill and Hingston Down outcrops must be the deeper of the two, because there is a small area of ground on the surface between them which has not been metamorphosed, roughly centred on the AA box at Sevenstones (A390).

An important feature of the granite ridges in this area are the east-west dykes of quartz-porphyry (elvan). These cut independently through both granite and metamorphic rocks. The quartz-porphyries of the West Country were generally formed 220-260 million years ago. There is one particularly long example in the Tamar valley which can be traced from the west side of Kit Hill, over the summit and eastwards as far as Hingston Down quarry. It is a vertical dyke of hard grey material, 58ft wide on the east side of the main Hingston Down quarry. The dyke can be traced across the floor into the old Parish Piece quarry, immediately to the west (now used for concrete block manufacture) where it comes down to a width of 38ft.

DYKES AND BRICKWORKS

The importance of these dykes was an economic one. Where they outcrop in the valley sides they form hard beds, often quarried as roadstone, but on the broad ridges they have been rotted to a sandy texture. Along the roadside which runs round the north side of the ridge from Hingston Down quarry towards Monks Cross, stands a line of works which developed these rotted elvans for firebrick and terracotta tile manufacture. The products were red or cream-coloured, due to the dykes being stained by hematite in parts, while in other places they were whitish-coloured and kaolinised like the country rock around them.

The old kilns can be seen best at Chilsworthy works. Tamar works to the west, now developed as a caravan park, provides a good view of the raw material in its pits on the opposite side of the road, while farther along the road Phoenix works is now marked only by a line of kiln archways in a field.

Coarse earthenware, articles like the cloam oven, was made at Calstock in the eighteenth century but the Hingston Down development followed the repeal of a tax on bricks in 1850. Its ruins are all the more remarkable when we recall that the output from one works alone ran at 80,000 bricks a week. The activity must have been enormous.

The red and cream terracotta tiles can be spotted in buttresses and continuous friezes on buildings all over the district, eg, a bank front in Callington, a house at the eastern end of Plympton St Maurice. They were also popular for tile paths in Plymouth gardens at one time.

FIG 70

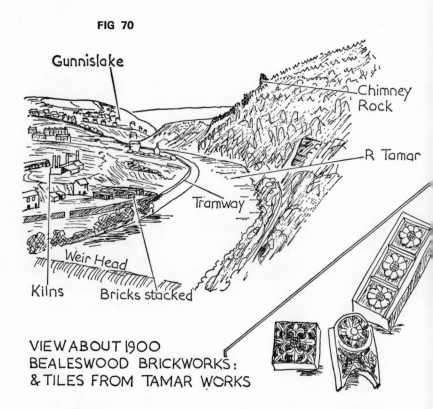

VIEW ABOUT 1900
BEALESWOOD BRICKWORKS:
& TILES FROM TAMAR WORKS

There were more brickworks down in the valley itself at Bealeswood below Gunnislake (Figure 70) and at Rumleigh on the Devon bank below Ganton. At the latter clay dumped on its valley floor by the Tamar was also used.

GRANITE QUARRYING

On the north side of Kit Hill is the now deserted Kit Hill

quarry. The stone here contains fewer large felspars than most Cornish granites. Although the working is now wired off, there are plenty of slabs just outside where the light-grey material can be examined. The colour is partly due to the amount of white mica in it. The quarry held many contracts in the nineteenth century and, when there were no orders for monumental work, like most granite quarries it resorted to sett making to keep going.

From the quarry make for the top of Kit Hill. The ornamental mine stack which dominates the summit was built with more architectural care than usual because of its commanding position. It remains now as a well-known landmark, preserved to carry a swarm of radio aerials.

Kit Hill is the best vantage point in the Tamar Valley, with extensive views in every direction. It emphasises the natural divisions of the valley used here. To the north, the river wanders down through rural landscapes to Horsebridge. Then comes the great barrier of the granite ridge. Extending eastwards from the viewpoint, its broad shoulders push the river east and out of sight.

To the south the valley opens out again and the path of the long estuary can be traced among the lines of ridges, though these are high enough to hide the river until it is beyond Saltash. There, a distant glint of water reveals the Hamoaze, and the wide break in the skyline beyond marks the limits of Plymouth Sound.

The large modern quarry at Hingston Down is out of sight over the ridge from Kit Hill. Its huge works straddle the roadside as the explorer returns to Dimson and higher Gunnislake. There is no parking space near the works and the visitor who has not obtained permission to enter should walk along the roadside railings where there is a view southwards into the main face.

The face is worked in four levels at present, though obviously the number increases with depth into the hillside. The granite is fine-grained, with few large felspars. Amethyst and copper pyrites occur in it; a lode of copper was exposed 45yd south of the road in the western face and another with some azurite is now visible in the eastern face. Tourmaline also appears in patches and veins. In the main face some of the tourmaline veins reach half an inch in width. The elvan

FIG 71

HINGSTON DOWN GRANITE QUARRY 410718 SW

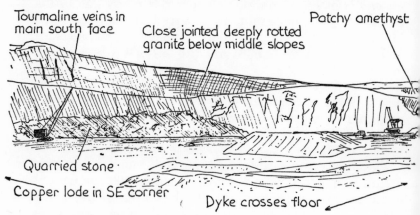

Tourmaline veins in main south face

Close jointed deeply rotted granite below middle slopes

Patchy amethyst

Quarried stone

Copper lode in SE corner

Dyke crosses floor

dyke, described above, is usually obscured by broken gravel on the quarry floor but it can be found quite easily.

The quarry reveals interesting features concerning joints and weathering. There is hardly any soil to clear from the surface here, which generally consists of about 5ft of shattered granite. Following the slope down the west face, the depth of rotting seems greatest in the centre (Figure 71). This confirms that groundwater circulation is the major agent of granite rotting. The amount of water present on the summit of the hill is smaller, but by the time the middle slopes are reached the amount of water running off has grown and greater damage occurs. However, below this level of the hillside, the steepening slopes get the extra volume of water away more quickly, and lessen the destruction once more.

There may be a link here with the rotting of the elvan dykes—the one supporting the brickworks described above lies just along this more readily rotted zone of the hillside. The convex slopes of Hingston Down have undoubtedly helped this weathering.

Hingston Down quarry can crush 250 tons of gravel per hour and supplies East Cornwall and West Devon. Its stone has a good polished-stone value, meaning that it wears well and does not become slippery in road works. For comparison, the Pebble Beds of East Devon are only suitable for foundations, whereas Hingston Down granite is of motorway standard. Grades ranging from 6in to sand size are made, and tarmac and concrete blocks. Cement for the latter is brought in from Plymstock, Plymouth.

Near the roadside, hidden in the heart of Gunnislake, is the old Pearson's quarry, worked 1808-1900 and eventually 130ft deep. Flooded now, its lake occasionally menaces the village homes below. Its granite was a valuable stone in many major projects, both local and national. The hardness of the granite at this end of the ridge was also a problem in widening the A390 road; blasting near the houses was difficult, and more time and money was expended than had been estimated.

GUNNISLAKE MINES

The very name of Gunnislake means a large pit or mine working and four local mines deserve mention because of their importance to the village, although not all of them are geological hunting-grounds today.

Right in the middle of the village is Gunnislake Old Mine, destined to be no more than a record on paper since its dumps and remaining building are soon to be cleared. It is a great pity geologically because it can provide some unusual specimens of radioactive uranites. The mine has been noted for apple-green flakes of torbernite, with its squarish tabular crystals and mica-like cleavage (a phosphate of uranium), and for the lemon- or orange-yellow zippeite which occurs in needles, rosettes or patches. Zippeite is another ore of uranium, named after a mineralogist, Professor Zippe.

North of the village, Gunnislake Clitters mine was worked in two sections, one near the river and the other high up near the old East Cornwall Mineral Railway line. Like Gunnislake Old Mine, the chief product was copper. The mine also produced arsenic from its own works near the river, and in the first world war wolfram was obtained from its dumps and those of the neighbouring Hingston Down Consols.

Hingston Down Consols provides ample evidence that the history of mining in Gunnislake may not have reached its final chapter for International Mine Services drilled a total of nearly 4,000ft in eight holes here on the south side of the ridge in 1968-9 and plan further work.

The dumps around Hitchings shaft show the living nature of geology—a new mineral, arthurite, was discovered there in 1954 by Sir Arthur Russell after whom it was named. A copper-iron arsenate, it occurs as thin apple-green crusts on the fragments of dumped granite.

MAP 27

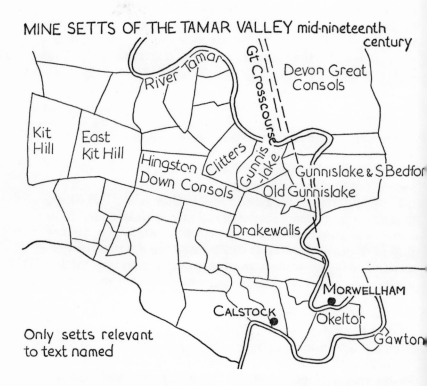

MINE SETTS OF THE TAMAR VALLEY mid-nineteenth century

Map 27 shows the divisions of the Gunnislake mining leases or setts in the mid-nineteenth century; the whole area was divided into mineral workings. Mines whose lodes were in alignment with neighbouring rich producers stood to attract the greatest investment—not to be followed by proportionately large returns in many cases! One of the most successful mines of the district was Drakewalls, by the roadside as you reach the top of the hill going westwards. On this site working was partly opencast because the tin produced occurred in a stock works near the surface and as lode mineral deep down. The surface pits were called gunnises by the miners, hence the name Gunnislake. Over its long life Drakewalls has produced a great variety of minerals : tin, copper and arsenic chiefly, but also lead, molybdenum, silver and wolfram.

MILLBROOK AND CAWSAND

The nature of the Tamar valley below the mining area has already been described in Chapter 12. Like so much of the Westcountry, these districts between the granite and the coast suffer from a comparative lack of rock exposures, and it is best to wait until the Tamar nears the sea.

The last great inlet on its ria before it enters Plymouth Sound is the one at Millbrook. Here the explorer might be justifiably surprised at seeing several large chimneys again but they are the remains of old brickworks, not mines. The brickworks used Middle Devonian slate beds from outcrops along the northern shore of Millbrook Lake. The material was crushed before moulding and firing; the same method is followed at the Pinhoe brickworks, Exeter, now but the Millbrook product was rather gritty and did not stand up to weathering well.

Today the Tamar finally comes to the sea at the mouth of

FIG 72

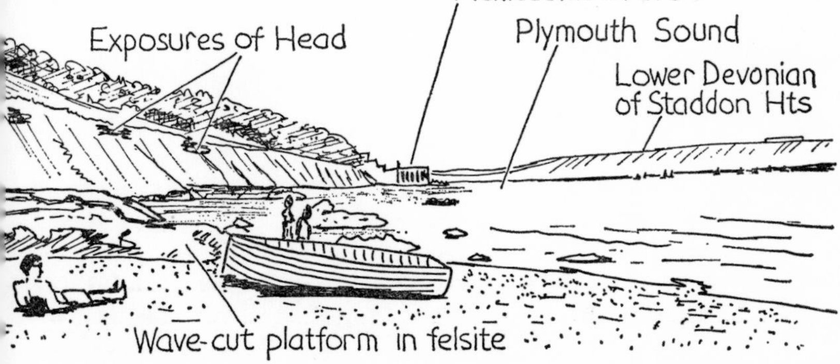

KINGSAND BEACH FELSITE 434505 NE

Picklecombe Fort

Exposures of Head

Plymouth Sound

Lower Devonian of Staddon Hts

Wave-cut platform in felsite

M

Plymouth Sound. It has only done so, however, for a brief 10,000 years in its long history, for only in the last 10,000 years has the sea been at its present position, partly flooding the old river valley and its tributaries. For a while previously, sea level was lower and the Tamar curved gently round the Sound, passing between a ridge (on which the Breakwater stands now) and Cawsand before it ran out westwards across land which now floors the Channel.

Along the present Cawsand shore one of the most interesting geological features is the exposure of felsite. The felsite outcrop, revealed in the beach and cliffs, also extends inland around Kingsand.

Felsite is a pink, fine-grained rock, chemically related to granite but volcanic (ie surface cooled) whereas granite is intrusive and cools below ground. Hence the very different

FIG 73

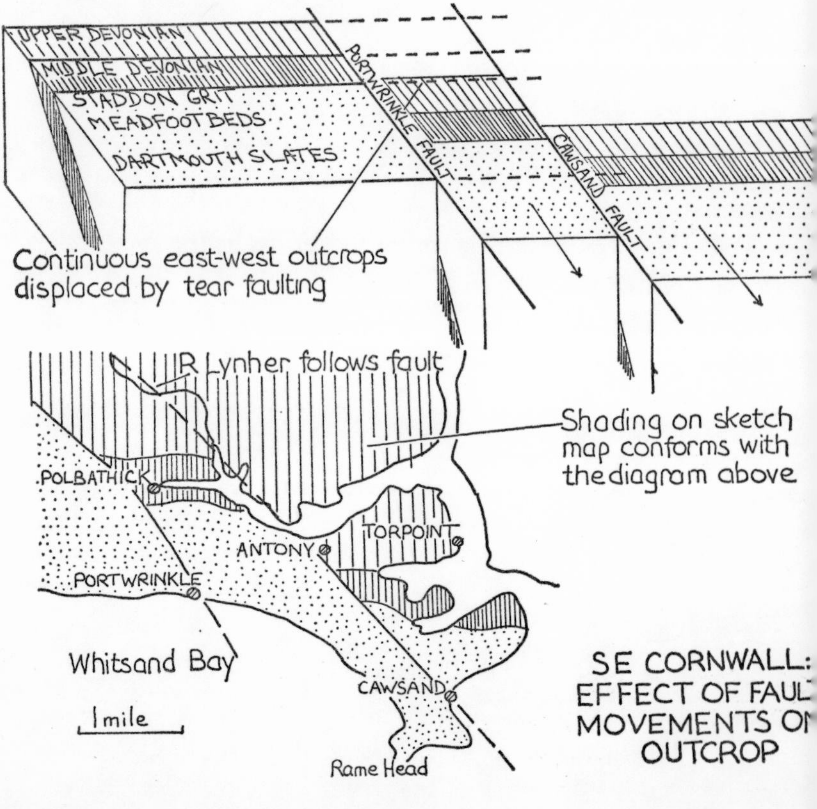

Continuous east-west outcrops displaced by tear faulting

R Lynher follows fault

Shading on sketch map conforms with the diagram above

SE CORNWALL: EFFECT OF FAULT MOVEMENTS ON OUTCROP

appearance of these two stones. Yet close inspection reveals
their chemical likeness more clearly, for felsite samples have
many specks of black mica in them and there are frequent
little whitish patches. These are kaolin minerals, the china
clay forming felspars of granite.

The cliffs above the beach platforms expose red earthy Head
material. The coastal track from Mount Edgecumbe park runs
along the top of the Head.

The western end of the felsite outcrop is marked by the
small stream which separates the twin villages of Kingsand
and Cawsand. This stream once had wider claims to fame as
it was formerly the boundary between Devon and Cornwall.
For geologists it is still important, since it is an example of
a fault-guided stream. This is illustrated in Figure 73, which
should also be related to Map 25 for it enlarges on the effect
of the NW-SE tear faults on the outcrops at Cawsand and to
the west.

If you take an east-west route through the latitude of Torpoint and Sheviock you would expect, in an area dominated
by east-west rock structures, to stay on the same formation all
the way. Instead, the journey is affected by the right-hand
displacement to the south of both the Cawsand and Portwrinkle faults. As you move west, each time you cross a fault
you step back in geological age to the previous formation. The
sequence runs : Upper Devonian at Torpoint, fault at Antony
and down to Lower Devonian Staddon and Meadfoot Beds,
fault near Tredrossel (or west of Polbathic if you prefer to
stick to the A38) and down to Lower Devonian Dartmouth
Slates.

In terms of landscape the effects of the faults vary. The
Cawsand fault certainly determines the trend of the coast
beyond the village of Penlee Point and, looking north-west on
the map, it has also influenced the course of the river Lynher.
The Portwrinkle fault may have effected the river Seaton in
similar fashion near Menheniot.

If the walker continues along the coast path to Penlee and
Rame Head, he will be able to compare the north coast of
the south-west peninsula with the southern. The South Cornwall and South Devon coasts are less rugged, their cliffs less
grand. There are larger beaches on these more indented shores
with their wider bays and estuaries. The north coast receives

M*

the full brunt of the Atlantic while the south is generally more sheltered.

Climbing to the old chapel at Rame Head there is a fine view of the sweep of Whitesand Bay to the west. Facing the prevailing south-westerly weather, this bay is perhaps the exception which proves the rule. It can be treacherous.

To the east the view takes in Penlee, the gap of the Sound and the Devon shore beyond. The Tamar has now reached the sea, carrying its loads of silt and sand to the bed to build new rocks for lands of the future. As you gaze at the sea from any clifftop you watch the surface of one of nature's greatest rock makers, and a sort of geological treasure-house!

MAP 28

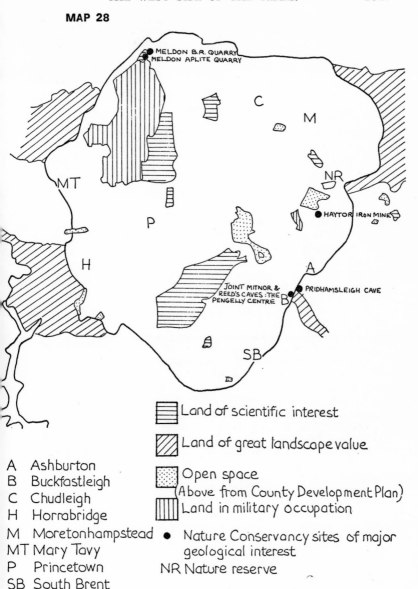

MELDON B.R. QUARRY
MELDON APLITE QUARRY

C

M

MT

NR

P

HAYTOR IRON MINE

H

A

JOINT MITNOR &
REED'S CAVES : THE
PENGELLY CENTRE

PRIDHAMSLEIGH CAVE

B

SB

	Land of scientific interest
	Land of great landscape value
	Open space

(Above from County Development Plan)

| | Land in military occupation |

● Nature Conservancy sites of major
geological interest

NR Nature reserve

A Ashburton
B Buckfastleigh
C Chudleigh
H Horrabridge
M Moretonhampstead
MT Mary Tavy
P Princetown
SB South Brent

AMENITY AND LAND OF SCIENTIFIC INTEREST

Glossary

AMMONITES—Coiled-shelled moluscs which existed from Triassic to late Cretaceous times. Ammonoids: coiled-shell dwellers.

ANTICLINE—Up-folded beds, arch-like, with the older layers inside the younger.

APATITE—Pale, sea-green mineral found in igneous rocks and in metamorphic rocks, particularly crystalline limestones. A natural phosphate.

APLITE—Fine-grained quartz and felspar rock formed by the consolidation of the last part of a granite intrusion.

BATHOLITH—The largest form of intrusion. Their various ages show they are part of the continual build-up of the earth's crust. They are buried features, uncovered by later erosion, and generally contain coarse-grained rocks, eg, granite.

BIOTITE—See **MICA.**

BLANKET BOG—Bogs are known as fen (pronounced 'vain' on Dartmoor) and are not to be confused with swamps (mires). The blanket bog is the continuous peat cover of the high moor, so there are two main areas of it on Dartmoor, the northern and southern.

CAINOZOIC—Literally the 'recent life', means the Tertiary era of geological time and includes Eocene, Oligocene, Miocene and Pliocene.

CHERT—Impure form of silica. Fresh specimens are light grey to black, but generally it is weathered yellow to brown. Its surfaces are less smooth and its fracture more splintery than flint, to which it is related.

CLEAVAGE—The way minerals split along planes related to their crystal structure, or the way certain fine-grained rocks split.

CLITTER—Loose, angular mass of boulders moved down-slope from destroyed tors by gravity, solifluction and frost-heaving.

COST BOOK—System of mine management sharing profit between the adventurers and demanding from them their proportion of any costs. Often led to the collapse of the mine if many refused to help out on some new project.

CULM—Name given to rocks of Coal Measure (Carboniferous) age in Devon. The thin beds of coal in them are referred to as Culm in early mine and trade accounts.

CUPOLA—Most simply described as a 'bump' or hump on the top of a batholith (above), where the molten material has stoped its way upwards into the cover of country rock above it.

DIP—Angle between the surface of a rock layer and a horizontal plane, measured in the direction of the plunge of the bed.

DOLERITE—Also known as greenstone. Hard, dark-green rock, formed by volcanic intrusions. Crystalline appearance.

DRIFT—Superficial deposits covering the solid rocks. Generally applied to clay and boulder deposits of ice-sheets and glaciers.

DYKE—Intrusive wall of rock; of molten origin. Vertical attitude, but may not be found so if involved in subsequent folding.

ESCARPMENT (SCARP)—Ridge with steep slope on one side (scarp-face) and gentle one on the other (dip-slope), being the end and upper surfaces respectively of a tilted formation.

FELSITE—Igneous rock, reddish-coloured, with quartz and felspars in it. Small flakes of mica and kaolinised patches can be found in it.

FELSPARS—Aluminium silicates basically; common rock-forming minerals and important in granite.

FLUORITE—(Fluorspar, Blue John, Derbyshire spar) Calcium fluoride. Ranges in colour from white to green, purple, yellow, blue; green is common on mine dumps. Occurs in veins with lead, zinc, quartz, barytes and tin.

FUMAROLE—Steam vent in the ground. Commonly part of the activity in hot-spring areas, all taken as signs of decaying volcanic activity.

GROWAN—Decomposed residue of granite weathering, consisting mainly of quartz.

HEAD—Mantle of rock waste washed downhill under cold climatic conditions, but widely used to describe any loose deposit.

HEMATITE—Steel grey to black-coloured iron ore but red-coloured in thin particles and earthy forms. Occurs also in specular, micaceous and kidney ore varieties.

IGNEOUS ROCKS—Rocks which were molten originally. Termed 'intrusive' if they formed below ground, 'extrusive', ie volcanic, if they did so at the surface.

INLIER—Area of older rock appearing up through surrounding of younger beds.

INTERGLACIAL—Warm climatic phase between two periods of glaciation. In the Ice Age there were four glaciations and three interglacial periods.

MESOZOIC—The 'middle life' era, containing the Triassic, Rhaetic, Jurassic and Cretaceous systems.

METAMORPHIC—Rocks which were originally sediments but have been transformed by contact with heat, pressure or active, migrating fluids.

MICA—Important mineral with a splendid lustre; splits into thin elastic plates. Black mica is called biotite, white mica is called muscovite.

OUTLIER—Detached patch of younger rock lying amidst older beds.

PALAEOZOIC—The era of 'ancient life', including Cambrian, Ordivician, Silurian, Devonian, Carboniferous and Permian systems.

PHENOCRYST—Large crystal contained in a finer-grained groundmass (See **PORPHYRITIC**).

PLEISTOCENE—The Ice Age, the earlier part of the Quaternary era in which we live today.

PORPHYRITIC—Term describing a rock with texture composed of two grain sizes; large crystals called phenocrysts, in a finer-grained groundmass.

QUARTZ—A very common mineral. Important in granite, common in veins. Forms bulk of sandstone; also flint, agate, chalcedony. Silicon dioxide (SiO_2).

QUARTZITE—Metamorphic rock, a re-crystallised sandstone largely formed of quartz; or a sandstone cemented by silica.

QUARTZ PORPHYRY—Known also as elvan, commonly occurs in dykes. Mainly quartz and felspar; fine-grained groundmass.

SEDIMENTARY ROCKS—Formed from the accumulated remains of other destroyed rocks and deposited naturally in seas, rivers, lakes.

SETT—Area of an old mining lease. Also name of granite blocks used in street paving.

SOLIFLUCTION (HILLWASH)—Soil creep, generally associated with the movement of thawed-out surface layers in cold climates, but the leaning headstones of any sloping churchyard will confirm that it occurs in present conditions to some extent.

STOCKWORKS—Ramification of thin veinlets and stringers of ore, with sporadic richer bunches, as opposed to a true mineral lode.

STRIKE—Direction or trend of a bed, measured at right angles to the direction of dip.

SYNCLINE—Down-folded structure in rocks, the older, lower beds surrounding the younger, upper ones in the centre.

TERTIARY—See **CAINOZOIC.**

TUFF—Rock formed of compacted volcanic ash.

UNCONFORMITY—A time break in the geological record, where rocks are not overlain by the next group in the geological succession.

WOLLASTONITE—Also known as Tabular spar. White, grey mineral produced by contact metamorphism of impure limestones.

XENOLITH—Fragment of rock absorbed into later intrusions and usually subjected to mineral replacement as a result.

Bibliography and References

GENERAL GEOLOGICAL INTEREST

Fossils: a little guide in colour (Paul Hamlyn)
Minerals: a little guide in colour (Paul Hamlyn)

Himus, G. W. *Dictionary of Geology* (Penguin)
Himus, G. W., and Sweeting, M. M. *Elements of Field Geology* (Univ Tutorial Press)
Mesozoic Fossils (British Museum, Natural History)
Palaeozoic Fossils (British Museum, Natural History)

DEVONSHIRE GEOLOGY

GENERAL

Exeter and Its Region (University of Exeter, for British Association meeting, 1969) especially Chapters 2 and 3
Proceedings of the Ussher Society
South West England, British Regional Geology, 3rd Edn (HMSO)
Some Present Views of Aspects of the Geology of Devon & Cornwall, (Commemorative volume for 1964, Royal Geological Society of Cornwall)
Transactions of Devonshire Association. Reports of Geological Section and Recorders reports, Geology

MINING BACKGROUND

Dines, H. G. *Metalliferous Mining Region of Southwest England*, 1956, vol 1 and 2 (HMSO). Detailed records of mines, output, material in the dumps and nature of mineralisation in the various districts
Earl, Bryan. *Cornish Mining* (Bradford Barton). A very readable account of mining techniques in recent eras. General application despite implication of title

Lewis, G. R. *The Stannaries* (Cambridge, Mass 1924, reprinted by Bradford Barton)

Plymouth Mineral & Mining Club Newsletters

Worth, R. H. *Dartmoor* (David & Charles), 'The Blowing House', pp 289-328

Salzmann, L. *English Industry in the Middle Ages*

DARTMOOR

Crossing, W. *The Dartmoor Worker*, Chapters on 'Peat Cutting', 'The Miner', 'The Quarryman', 'The Clay Labourer'.

Dartmoor Essays (Devonshire Association)

Geology of Dartmoor, Memoirs Geological Survey for Sheet 338, 1912, (HMSO)

Geology of the Country around Ivybridge & Modbury, Memoirs Geological Survey for Sheet 349, 1912 (HMSO)

Geology of the Country around Okehampton, Memoirs Geological Survey for Sheet 324, 1968 (HMSO)
Memoirs for the Teignmouth Sheet (339) and Exeter Sheet (325) cover small areas of the eastern margin of Dartmoor

Harris, Helen. *Industrial Archaeology of Dartmoor*, (David & Charles), for details of former mine and quarry sites

Worth, R. H. *Dartmoor* (David & Charles). Chapters on the 'Physical Geography of Dartmoor' and 'The Moorstone Age'

TAMAR VALLEY

Barton, D. B. *Mines & Mineral Railways of East Cornwall & West Devon* (Bradford Barton)

Booker, F. L. *Industrial Archaeology of the Tamar Valley*, (David & Charles). Fascinating and thorough account of the mining activity in the nineteenth century

Geology of the Country around Plymouth & Liskeard, Memoirs Geological Survey for Sheet 348, 1907 (HMSO)

Geology of the Country around Tavistock & Launceston, Memoirs Geological Survey, for Sheet 337, 1911 (HMSO)

Jenkin, A. K. Hamilton. *Mines and Miners of Cornwall*, Parts 14 and 15

SHORT LIST OF REFERENCES & USEFUL PAPERS

Blyth, F. G. H. 'The Lustleigh Fault in north-east Dartmoor',

Geol Mag, 94 (1957) pp 291-6

Blyth, F. G. H. 'The Structure of the north-eastern tract of the Dartmoor Granite' *Quart Jour Geol Soc*, 118 (1962), pp 435-53

Brammall, A. 'The Dartmoor Granite', *Proc Geol Assoc*, 37 (1926) pp 251-77

Bott, M. H. P., Day, A. A., and Masson Smith D., 'The geological interpretation of gravity and magnetic surveys in Devon and Cornwall' *Phil Trans Roy Soc A*, 251 (1958) pp 161-91

Brunsden, D. 'Denudation Chronology of the River Dart', *Trans Inst Brit Geogrs*, 32 (1963) pp 49-63

Brunsden, D. et al 'Denudation Chronology of Parts of S. W. England', *Field Studies*, 2 No 1 (1964) pp 115-32

Broughton, D. G. 'Tin working in the eastern district of the parish of Chagford, Devon', *Proc Geol Assoc*, 78 (1967), pp 447-62

Dearman, W. R. 'The structure of the Culm Measures at Meldon, near Okehampton, Devon', *Quart Jour Geol Soc*, 115 (1959), pp 65-106

Dearman, W. R. 'Dartmoor' Guide No 33, *Geologists Assoc*, 1962. (Provides excursion details, mainly for NW Dartmoor)

Dearman, W. R. 'Wrench faulting in Cornwall and South Devon', *Proc Geol Assoc*, 74 (1964), pp 265-87

Dearman, W. R. and Butcher, N. E. 'The Geology of the Devonian and Carboniferous Rocks of the North-west border of the Dartmoor Granite, Devonshire', *Proc Geol Assoc*, 70 (1959), pp 51-92

Dineley, D. L. 'The Devonian System in South Devonshire', *Field Studies*, No 1 (1961), pp 121-40

Exley, C. S. and Stone, M. 'The granite rocks of South-west England', *Roy Geol Soc Cornwall* (1964), pp 131-84

Goodridge, J. C. 'Devon Great Consols; a study in Victorian mining enterprise', *Trans Dev Assoc*, 96 (1964), pp 228-68

Green, J. F. N. 'The History of the River Dart, Devon', *Proc Geol Assoc*, 60 (1949), pp 105-24

House, M. R. and Selwood, E. B. 'Palaeozoic palaeontology in Devon and Cornwall', *Roy Geol Soc Cornwall* (1964), pp 45-86

Linton, D. L. 'The Problem of Tors', *Geogr Journ,* 121 (1955), pp 470-87

Selwood, E. B. 'Ammonoids and trilobites from the Upper Devonian and lowest Carboniferous of the Launceston area of Cornwall', *Palaeontology* 3 pt 2 (1960), pp 153-85

Simmons, I. G. 'An outline of the vegetation history of Dartmoor', *Trans Dev Assoc,* 94 (1962), pp 555-74

Spargo, T. *'The Mines of Cornwall and Devon: Statistics and Observations',* London, 1865

Toll, R. W. 'The Arsenic Industry in West Devon' *Mining Magazine* August, 1953

Woolner, Diana H. 'Peat Charcoal' *Jour Hist Industry and Technology,* 3 (1966), pp 270-1

Woolner, Diana H. 'Peat Charcoal', *Devon & Cornwall Notes & Queries,* 30 (1965-7), pp 118-20 and pp 252-3 (John Roberts)

Worth, R. H. Presidential address, *Trans Dev Assoc,* 62 (1930) 49 (Dartmoor peat deposits)

Appendix: GENERALISED TABLE OF STRATA MENTIONED IN THE TEXT

Period	Division	Launceston	Meldon/Okehampton	Middle Teign valley
Quaternary (1-1½ M years ago)	HOLOCENE PLEISTOCENE	Sands and earths / Clitters, head, river gravels, terrace deposits		

Mineralisation continued, probably in a series of actions, down to 75 M years ago
Dartmoor granite intruded during folding of the region 290-295 M years ago

Period	Division	Launceston	Meldon/Okehampton	Middle Teign valley
CARBONIFEROUS (270-350 M years ago: duration 80 M)	Upper	*Launceston* Trebursye Beds	*Meldon/Okehampton* Crackington Formation (sandstones, many 100'sft thick)	*Middle Teign valley* Kiddens Formation / Ashton Formation } Shales & cherts / Spara Bridge Formation 300-700ft thick
	Lower	Cannapark limestones and Barracados Cherts	Meldon Calcareous group, 250ft / Meldon Shales, quarzites & volcanics, 4-500ft / Meldon Slates with lenticles, + 400ft (Upper Devonian not represented at Meldon and Okehampton)	Teign Cherts and lavas 100-150ft / Combe Shales (black) 300-500ft / Trusham shales, 200ft
DEVONIAN (350-400 M years ago: duration 50 M)	Upper	Yeolmbridge Beds / Stourscombe Beds / Petherwin Beds		Hyner shales and siliceous nodules
	Middle	Middle Devonian limestones and contemporary tuffs and lavas / Middle Devonian shales		
	Lower	Staddon Grits / Meadfoot Beds / Dartmouth Slates		

Palaeozoic

Times given above are in millions of years (M). For each geological period, remember that this table is not a complete record since only those strata mentioned in the text or featured in diagrams are given.

Acknowledgements

I wish to record sincere thanks to Dr E. B. Selwood for his guidance and comment on the bulk of the material included here and to Dr W. R. Dearman for reading and commenting on some of the West Dartmoor sections, particulary the Meldon area. I am most grateful to Mr G. Bisson, District Officer of the Institute of Geological Sciences; to Mr D. A. Bassett of the Amalgamated Roadstone Corporation, Hingston Down quarry; to Mr W. Stevens of English China Clays, Lee Moor division; to Mr F. W. Olver for information on Smallhanger clayworks; and to Mr J. Pope for loan of reference material.

In the Tamar Valley where, in contrast to Dartmoor, most of the land is in private ownership, I am indebted to Mr Hatt of Tavistock Woodlands and many landowners who gave permission for access to mine dumps and other features of interest. Many former miners and quarrymen have given me information and their friendly help has been a highlight of field days. My wife has given me invaluable help in many ways and Mrs J. I. Neale has been a most efficient typist.

Map 12 is based on the map in H. G. Dines' *Metalliferous Mining Region of South West England,* HMSO 1956, page 722, and Map 21 on the pull-out map XI from the same work. Any geological study inevitably draws on the published maps and memoirs of the Institute of Geological Sciences and grateful acknowledgement is made to the Director for permission to use them.

JOHN W. PERKINS

Index